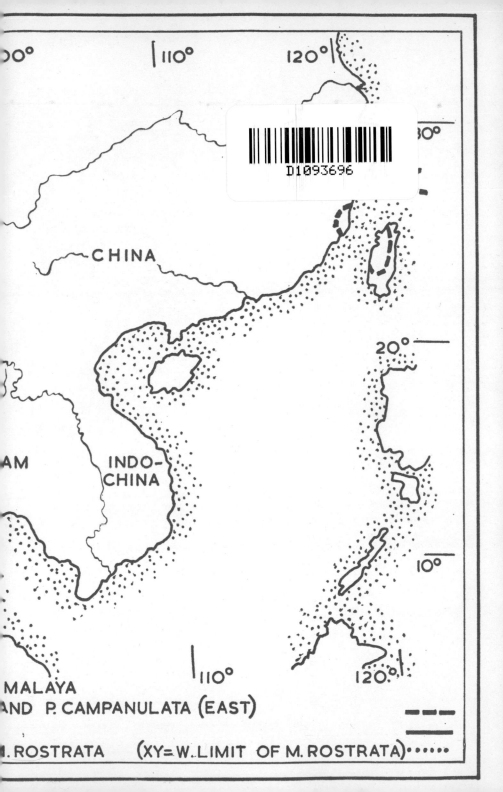

100° |110°   120°| 80°

CHINA

20°

INDO-
CHINA

AM

10°

|110°

120°|

MALAYA
AND P. CAMPANULATA (EAST)

.ROSTRATA   (XY=W.LIMIT OF M.ROSTRATA)······

Pilgrimage for Plants

Frank Kingdon-Ward, Ukhrul, Manipur State, 1948

Pilgrimage for Plants

by

Frank Kingdon-Ward

O.B.E. M.A. F.L.S. V.M.H.

Gold Medallist and Hon. Life Fellow of the Royal Geographical Society, and of the Royal Horticultural Society of London, Gold Medallist of the Royal Scottish Geographical Society, and of the Massachusetts Horticultural Society, U.S.A., Hon. Life Member of the Royal Central Asian Society and of the Pennsylvania Horticultural Society, U.S.A., and Hon. Freeman of the Worshipful Company of Gardeners of the City of London

With a Biographical Introduction

and Bibliography

by

William T. Stearn

George G. Harrap & Co. Ltd
London Toronto Wellington Sydney

For

ELIZABETH BARRACLOUGH

Formerly of the British Embassy in Rangoon, a dear friend, who, on my two last journeys into Burma, did so much to help us and make our visit to Rangoon pleasant and memorable

First published in Great Britain 1960
by George G. Harrap & Co. Ltd
182 High Holborn, London, W.C.1

© *Jean Kingdon-Ward, 1960*

Composed in Intertype Times and printed by
The Garden City Press Limited
Letchworth, Hertfordshire

Made in Great Britain

Acknowledgments

My sincere thanks are due to all those, and they are many, who have helped me consciously or otherwise. To Dr George Taylor, Director of the Royal Botanic Gardens, Kew, and his staff; to Mr J. E. Dandy, Keeper of Botany at the British Museum (Natural History), London; to Mr F. Ludlow, Mr W. T. Stearn, and others, I am indebted for the correct naming of many plants, and other invaluable help. To the Royal Geographical Society I owe the quotation from the *Geographical Journal* on pp. 49–50.

To my friend Lady O'Malley (Ann Bridge), who always maintains that scientists cannot write English, I and the book owe much. She devotedly went through the whole manuscript, using her unrivalled literary skill and experience to smooth and polish the occasional asperities of its prose.

Finally to my wife Jean I am everlastingly indebted, not only for four typings of the book before I was completely satisfied, but even more for the memorable part she played in the events described in three of the chapters—"Glorious Dogwood," "Lilies in the Sun," and "In Search of Tea"—not to mention several other plants described, in which she shared.

F. K.-W.

Note

I am especially indebted to Mr W. T. Stearn of the Natural History Museum, London, for the list of my husband's publications that comes at the end of this book, as well as for his biographical introduction. It will be of the greatest help to botanists, gardeners, geographers, and others interested in my husband's work. This collection of his last essays on the plants and wilds of eastern Asia has thus become a useful summary of his travels and writings. I have accordingly appended to it as a further expression of his interests an essay on "Geography and Living Standards in South-east Asia."

J. K.-W.

Contents

Illustrations

PLATES IN HALF-TONE

LINE ILLUSTRATIONS IN THE TEXT

Biographical Introduction

FRANK KINGDON-WARD[1] was born on November 6, 1885, made his first plant-collecting journey into the wilds of eastern Asia in 1911, returned from his last journey in 1957, and died in London on April 8, 1958. His work as a collector of seeds for gardens and specimens for botanical institutions thus spanned forty-five years—a proud record unlikely to be excelled in the difficult region of north Burma, Assam, western China, and south-east Tibet, which he traversed so many times. He knew that not even a lifelong succession of expeditions —he made twenty-two—could reveal, let alone exploit, all the floral riches of such an area; hence, no matter the hardships and disappointments of previous journeys, he was ever eager to return there. He began early; even as a boy he camped by himself. All his life he manifested the same independence of spirit, the same love of the open air, the same interest in natural history. Writing from first-hand knowledge, Dr N. L. Bor has truly observed that "those who are prepared to accept the penalties of one-man exploration—the physical hardship, the utter loneliness of months in a strange land among strange people, the nauseating dullness of a diet of *tsampa* [flour ground from roasted grains of barley] washed down with rancid butter tea and all the inconvenience of travelling 'light'—must possess exceptional courage, determination, loyalty to their sponsors, and devotion to their purpose. These qualities, combined with modesty—for all the great explorers were modest men—are

[1] His father's surname was *Ward*, his mother's before marriage was *Kingdon*; his name at registration of birth was *Ward, Francis Kingdon*, but in his later years (from 1946 onwards) he preferred *Kingdon-Ward, Frank*. His friends called him Frank, Ward, and Kingdon Ward without much consistency.

qualities which make men great, and Kingdon-Ward possessed them in full measure."

He owed his initiation into botany to his father, Professor Harry Marshall Ward (1854–1906), whose early death deprived British botany of one of its leading research workers and Cambridge of an enterprising and stimulating teacher, the founder of its modern Botany School. Marshall Ward spent the years 1880–82 in Ceylon investigating the coffee-leaf disease. In 1883 he married Mary Kingdon, of Exeter. Their son Francis Kingdon was born at Withington, Lancashire, in 1885, the year of Marshall Ward's appointment as Professor of Botany at the Royal Indian Engineering College at Cooper's Hill, Surrey, England. Ten years later the family moved to Cambridge, Marshall Ward having been appointed Professor of Botany in succession to Babington. Frank received his schooling at St Paul's School, Hammersmith, then entered the University of Cambridge in October 1904 as an undergraduate member of Christ's College, took honours in the Natural Sciences Tripos in 1906, and went out to China early in 1907 as a school-teacher at the Shanghai Public School. When the ship stopped at Singapore he slipped ashore and passed the first of his many nights outdoors under a tropical sky. In 1909 he broke his three-year contract with the school in order to travel across central and western China, to Kangting (Tatsienlu) and into Kansu, with an American zoologist, Malcolm P. Anderson. This journey was in no way a botanical expedition. Young Ward nevertheless made a small collection of botanical specimens which he gave to the Botany School, Cambridge, and which were identified and listed by R. S. Adamson in the *Journal of Botany* (*London*) Vol. 51, pp. 129–131 (April 3, 1913). Of the three supposed new species described in this first enumeration of specimens collected by Ward in eastern Asia, *Gueldenstaedtia flava* Adamson has slight priority over *G. tongolensis* Ulbrich (April 15, 1913), but *Vaccinium wardii* Adamson is now considered synonymous with *V. fragile* Franchet (1895), and *Jasminum wardii* Adamson with *J. beesianum* Diels (1912). It is, however, a not inappropriate coincidence that the names of Ward and Bees should thus be linked, for in 1911 Messrs Bees of Liverpool engaged him as their collector in north-west Yunnan, the richness of which as a field for horticultural enterprise had been proved by their previous collector, George Forrest (1873–1932).

From then onward Ward became a professional plant-collector, explorer, and author. His scientific training and natural aptitude gave him a keen interest not simply in the botany but also in the geography as a whole of the regions in which he worked; he surveyed and mapped as well as collected. He possessed, moreover, a romantic temperament which needed a literary outlet; as he travelled, his mind continually sought and found words to register his experiences, to convey to others his impressions of the changing scenery, the beauty of the flowers, the incidents of the journey. By such activity a sensitive traveller becomes ever more receptive, ever more observant, and sustains his own morale, for he can talk in his own language to paper, amid peoples who understand not a word of it, and he can find thereby a companionship with distant countrymen through days of dullness and discomfort. Thanks to this gift, his skill as a photographer, and the traditional interest of the British public in travel-books, his journeys are remarkably well-documented. Almost every one provided him with material for a book or a series of articles, as well as seeds for his horticultural subscribers, and herbarium specimens for botanical institutions. It is thus easy to compile a chronological record. The following summary is based on the account in E. H. M. Cox, *Plant Hunting in China*, pp. 181–183 (1945), for the years 1911–39, but supplemented by references to books giving more detailed information about the journeys and to botanical papers listing the plants collected.

1909–10. WESTERN CHINA, from Shanghai to Kangting (Tatsienlu) and into south Kansu. Plants enumerated by R. S. Adamson, "Plants from Western China," *Journal of Botany (London)* Vol. 51, pp. 129–131 (1913). Journey made with M. P. Anderson.

1911. NORTH YUNNAN and TIBET (SIKANG), by way of Tengchung (Tengueh) Tali, Weihsi, Tsuku (on the Mekong River), Atuntzu, Menkong (on the Salween River), over the Doker-la, back to the Mekong, up to Atuntzu, Moting (on the Yangtze), Tsa-lei, north to Batang (Paan), later to Gartok, then to the Mekong, back to Tengchung. Described in *The Land of the Blue Poppy: Travels of a Naturalist in Eastern Tibet* (1913). Collecting numbers, 1–200.

1913. YUNNAN and TIBET (SIKANG), by way of Myitkyina, Tengchung, Tali, Likiang (Lichiang), Chungtien plateau, Atuntzu, over the Doker-la, Kagurbu, Beima-shan (Pai-ma-shan), Tibetan part of the Mekong–Salween divide (Tsarong), down the Salween, across the Salween–N'mai-hka divide, back over the Pitu-la to Atuntzu. Described in *The Mystery Rivers of Tibet* (1923). Collecting numbers include 260–793.

1914. NORTH BURMA, by way of Myitkyina, Hpimaw, Feng-shweling, Imaw Bum, Wulaw pass, Shingrup-chet, Fort Hertz, back to Myitkyina. Described in *In Farthest Burma* (1921). Collecting numbers presumably 1000–3000.

1919. NORTH BURMA, to Imaw Bum and Hpimaw. Collecting numbers include 3038–3721.

1921. YUNNAN and SZECHWAN, by way of Tali, Likiang, Yungning, Muli, thence into Szechwan, then back to Tengchung and Bhamo. Described in *From China to Hkamti Long* (1924), *The Romance of Plant Hunting* (1924). Collecting numbers include 3776–5005.

1922. YUNNAN and SZECHWAN, TIBET and NORTH BURMA, by way of Bhamo, Tengchung, Tali, Yungning, Muli, Likiang, Kari pass, Beima-shan, Atuntzu, Takala, across the Mekong-Salween divide, Chamutong, across to the Taron River and the Nam Tamai River, Fort Hertz, Myitkyina. Described in *From China to Hkamti Long* (1924) and articles in *The Gardeners' Chronicle* (1922–23). Collecting numbers include 5384–5602.

1924–25. EASTERN HIMALAYA (BHUTAN) and SOUTHERN TIBET, by way of Sikkim, Phari, Gyantze, the Tsangpo valley, Tsangpo Gorge, Bhutan, back to India. Described in *The Riddle of the Tsangpo Gorges* (1926) and articles in *The Gardeners' Chronicle* (1924–26). Journey made in company with the Right Hon. the Earl of Cawdor. Primulas enumerated by W. W. Smith and Ward in *Notes of the Royal Botanical Garden, Edinburgh* Vol. 15, pp. 69–98 (1926); other plants by C. V. B. Marquand and H. K. Airy-Shaw in *Journal of the Linnean Society of London, Bot.* Vol. 48, pp. 149–229 (1929). Collecting numbers include 5623–6430.

1926. NORTH BURMA and ASSAM, by way of Myitkyina, Fort Hertz, Nam Tamai, Seinghku, Diphuk-la, Lohit (Luhit) valley, to Sadiya. Described in *Plant Hunting on the Edge of the World* (1930) and articles in *The Gardeners' Chronicle* (1926–28). Collecting numbers include 6605–7698.

1927–28. ASSAM, MISHMI HILLS. Described in *Plant Hunting on the Edge of the World* (1930). Collecting numbers include 7701–8754.

1929. BURMA and INDO-CHINA. March and April spent in the southern Shan States, Burma, and May and June in upper Laos, Indo-China, with the William V. Kelley-Roosevelts Expedition to Eastern Asia for the Field Museum of Chicago. 400 specimens. See *Plant Hunting in the Wilds* (1931).

1930–31. NORTH BURMA and BURMA–TIBET FRONTIER, by way of Myitkyina, Fort Hertz, Nam Tamai, Adung valley, Namni-la, and back by same route to Myitkyina. Described in *Plant Hunter's Paradise* (1937) and articles in *The Gardeners' Chronicle* (1932–33). Collecting numbers, 9001–10239.

1933. ASSAM and TIBET (SIKANG), by way of Sadiya, Lohit valley, Rima, Rong-tö Chu valley, Shugden Gompa, the Salween, Rong-tö-Chu valley, over into top of Delei valley, Lohit valley, back to Sadiya. Described in *A Plant Hunter in Tibet* (1934) and partly in Ronald Kaulback's *Tibetan Trek* (1936). Collecting numbers, 10300–11078.

1935. ASSAM and TIBET, between latitude 28 degrees–31 degrees and longitude 92 degrees–95 degrees. Described in *Assam Adventure* (1941) and in articles in *The Gardeners' Chronicle* (1936–37). Collecting numbers include 11100–12586.

1937. NORTH BURMA and TIBET, by way of Myitkyina, Fort Hertz, Nam Tamai, Adung valley, Gamlang valley, Ka Karpo Razi, and back by same route to Myitkyina. Described in *Burma's Icy Mountains* (1949) and articles in *The Gardeners' Chronicle* (1938–39). Collecting numbers include 12600–13573.

1938. ASSAM, BALIPARA FRONTIER TRACT. Described in *Assam Adventure* (1941). Collecting numbers include 13588–14360.

1938–39. NORTH BURMA, by way of Myitkyina, Htawgaw, Imaw Bum, Hpimaw, Panwa pass, Hpare pass, back to Myitkyina. Described in "The Vernay–Cutting Expedition, November 1938 to April 1939, Report," *Brittonia* Vol. 4, pp. 1–19 (1941). Plants enumerated by E. D. Merrill in *Brittonia* Vol. 4, pp, 20–188 (1941). Collecting numbers, Vernay–Cutting (Ward) 1–531.

1946. ASSAM, Khasi Hills. Collecting numbers include 16018–16091.

1948. ASSAM, East Manipur. Described in *Plant Hunter in Manipur* (1952). Collecting numbers, 17001–18375.

1949. ASSAM, Mishmi Hills, Khasi Hills, Naga Hills. Collecting numbers, 18376–18850.

1950. ASSAM and TIBET, by way of Sadiya, up the Lohit valley, Walong to Rima and back. Described in Jean Kingdon-Ward's *My Hill so Strong* (1952). Collecting numbers include 19205–20300.

1953. NORTH BURMA, by way of Myitkyina and Sumprabum to Hkinlum and back. Described in *Return to the Irrawaddy* (1956). Collecting numbers include 20301–21716, plus 100 numbers from 22001–22100.

1956. WEST CENTRAL BURMA, southern Chin Hills, Mount Victoria. Collecting numbers include 21726–22884 (less the 100 numbers mentioned above).

1956–57. CEYLON. Collecting numbers, 22901–23068.

Ward's 1909–10 specimens are at the Botany School, Cambridge, England, those of 1913–22 at the Royal Botanic Garden, Edinburgh, of 1924–28 at the Royal Botanic Gardens, Kew, of 1929 at the Chicago Natural History Museum, of 1930–38 and 1946–57 at the British Museum (Natural History), London, of 1938–39 at the New York Botanical Garden, with some duplicate specimens in other herbaria, notably in Gothenburg Botanical Garden, Sweden, those of 1956–57.

Ward was accompanied on his 1924–25 expedition by Lord Cawdor, on his 1928 expedition by H. M. Clutterbuck, on his 1930 expedition by Lord Cranbrook. Ronald Kaulback went with him as far as Zayul in 1933. His first marriage was dissolved in 1937. In 1947 he married Miss Jean Macklin, whose enthusiasm for plants and travel matched his own, and she accompanied him on all his subsequent expeditions, contributing much to their success. Only those who have made a plant-collecting expedition can know how much labour it involves above the usual camp tasks; reaching and gathering the plants is merely the first stage; then follows the much less exciting business of attaching labels, writing field-notes and diary, changing the drying papers and going over the specimens, packing them and protecting against mould and vermin, as well as cleaning and packeting seed, often by a dim, fitful lantern-light and in wet weather, after a tiring day in the jungle or bush, when the collector longs to rest. Much of this unavoidable work cannot be delegated to inexperienced native helpers, however willing. Mrs Kingdon-Ward quickly became expert in such things and proved an invaluable assistant, as her husband often gratefully acknowledged.

During the First World War he served in the Indian Army, attaining the rank of captain. He was in Burma during the Second World War when the Japanese invaded the country, but, following routes known to him from his peace-time exploration, he escaped without much difficulty into India. Here he taught the armed forces about survival in the jungle. Immediately after the war the United States Government employed him to search for the wreckage of American planes and bodies of airmen who had crashed when flying from India to China. It was during one of these missions that in January 1946 he found the remains of a liliaceous plant on Mount Sirhoi in Manipur, which discovery led to the introduction of *Lilium mackliniae*.

In addition to the books listed above, Kingdon-Ward also wrote *The Loom of the East* (1932), *The Romance of Gardening* (1935), *Modern Exploration* (1945), *About this Earth* (1946), *Commonsense Rock Gardening* (1948), *Rhododendrons and Azaleas* (1949), *Footsteps in Civilization* (1950), *Berried Treasure* (1954), and many articles in horticultural periodicals, notably *The Gardeners' Chronicle*, as well as papers in learned journals such as the *Annals of Botany, Proceedings of the Linnean Society of London*, the Royal Geographical Society's *Geographical Journal, Royal Central Asian Journal*, etc.

Although it is too early to assess the value to geography, botany, horticulture, and travel-literature of Kingdon-Ward's life-work, at least it received recognition in his life-time. Thus he added many names and contour-lines to maps which would otherwise have been blank or indefinite, and the Royal Geographical Society honoured him in 1930 with its Founder's Gold Medal and the Royal Scottish Geographical Society in 1936 with the Livingstone Gold Medal. His botanical collections at the same time made known the general character and affinities of the vegetation, and provided material for the description of many species new to science. The Linnean Society of London accordingly invited him to deliver the 1936 Hooker Lecture, "A sketch of the vegetation and geography of Tibet" (*Proceedings of the Linnean Society of London*, Vol. 148 (1935-36): pp. 133–159; 1936). The names of the genera *Kingdon-wardia* (Gentianaceae) and *Wardaster* (Compositae), the epithet *kingdonii* given to species of *Allium, Gentiana* and *Saxifraga*, the epithet *wardii* to species of *Acer, Aeschynanthus, Agapetes, Anemone, Arisaema, Berberis, Buddleja, Calanthe, Camellia, Corydalis, Cotoneaster, Cremanthodium, Cyananthus, Cypripedium, Eurya, Gaultheria, Gentiana, Ilex, Justicia, Lilium, Lindera, Lonicera, Lychnis, Micromeria, Myricaria, Orchis, Paphiopedilum, Pedicularis, Petrocosmea, Primula, Rhododendron, Rubus, Salvia, Saxifraga, Sorbus, Strobilanthes, Tsuga* and *Viburnum* and the epithet *kingdonwardii* to a species of *Prunus* testify to the appreciation by systematic botanists of the wealth of new plants brought by him from eastern Asia. Most of the introductions into gardens by any collector fail to persist after the novelty of raising them has dimmed and climate and weather have played havoc with them over a few years. However, in *Primula florindae, Cotoneaster conspicuus, Meconopsis betonicifolia* var. *baileyi*, and

Lilium mackliniae, as well as in many rhododendrons, Kingdon-Ward introduced plants which give every indication of being permanent additions to temperate gardens. His success led the Royal Horticultural Society to award him in 1932 its highest honour, the Victoria Medal of Honour in Horticulture, as well as the Veitch Memorial Medal in 1933, and to dedicate to him Volume 162 (1940) of *Curtis's Botanical Magazine*. In 1952 he received the Order of the British Empire for his services to horticulture. These honours came from his fellow-countrymen. Equally gratifying was the George Robert White Memorial Medal awarded him in 1934 by the Massachusetts Horticultural Society.

Pilgrimage for Plants has thus a unique background of experience. A series of essays mostly centring on a plant or group of plants of special interest, it blends fragments of autobiography and speculations on plant-geography with first-hand accounts of the plants themselves in their natural habitats and their introduction into gardens. Kingdon-Ward's love of the high mountains runs through it all. Scarcely a week before his sudden unexpected death he was discussing with me the possibilities of a plant-collecting expedition into the Caucasus or northern Persia; he was also planning one to Vietnam. It is hard to believe that the rough hill trails will know his lean, tough frame no more.

WILLIAM T. STEARN

DEPARTMENT OF BOTANY,
BRITISH MUSEUM (NATURAL HISTORY),
LONDON

·1·

One Long Holiday

YOUR life must be one long holiday! "
I had just given a lecture on plant-hunting in Tibet;
after listening eagerly a woman came up to me and made
this remark. I sometimes think now that there may have been a
certain amount of truth in what she said; I didn't think so at the
time. I had shown slides of beautiful flowers unknown in Europe,
of nameless snow mountains and glaciers, roaring rivers and
aspiring forests; the people of the great hills too, smiling and
friendly as they are—and it would ill become a lecturer to spoil
such scenes with complaints of trials and tribulations, or accounts
of endless uncongenial chores, and frequent disappointments and
frustrations; I had not done so. But perhaps the lady really meant
'holiday' in its more fundamental sense. A change of occupation
can be just as much of a holiday as no occupation at all.

I became a botanical explorer partly by chance and good luck,
and remained one wholly by choice. Twice in fifteen years I was
given an opportunity to be done with it and earn my living by
more conventional and less intermittent work. On each occasion
I was offered a permanent official position in the world of
botany, either of which from almost any point of view would
have suited me admirably. The first offer came unexpectedly
after a disastrous year's journey in the very days when I was
learning; and the temptation to abandon plant-hunting was
strong. The second came equally unexpectedly after a highly successful journey, when I could have retired with honour. I could
hardly expect to repeat my recent triumph, at least for some
time, and the next journey was bound to be an anti-climax.
Nevertheless I refused the second offer also, though with real
regret. After that I became set in my ways, and my friends gave
me up as incorrigible. A good many years passed before I was

offered honourable retirement and a small Government pension;
since then I have made, with my wife, five more journeys.

For some unexplained reason I was drawn to botanical exploration from an early age. Before I entered the University of Cambridge I read Schimper's *Plant Geography*, which is richly illustrated with beautiful pictures of the different types of forest,
especially tropical forest. These illustrations made a deep impression on me, and burnt on my heart a profound desire to see for
myself the tropical forest region. Moreover, I was impatient.
Instead of waiting for the university appointment I might have
hoped to get, I accepted the first job which promised to take me
to those hot and blissful lands far off. The job had nothing whatever to do with biology; but at least I should see the tropics.

All the pictures I had seen of those regions suggested the
mysterious landscapes for which I craved. I was not in the least
sophisticated; it surprised me to learn that I should almost touch
the equator *en route* to my new home! As it happened, the whole
time we were in the tropics we were at sea, except for three days
in Singapore and one in Hongkong. But those three days in
Singapore within two degrees of the equator were Adventure.
They were pure Schimper. At last I had my heart's desire.

The youth of to-day, of course, can steep themselves in a
tropical atmosphere without leaving the high street. The cinema
and television have made the Guiana forest and the Congo as
familiar as Piccadilly. Indeed, the film industry is getting worried
as to where to look for fresh fields to conquer. Almost every
possible location in the world has been exploited. But before the
days of the cinema everything was unfamiliar, and therefore
exciting, even the traveller's-tree (*Ravenala madagascariensis*)
—a banal near-banana to many of us nowadays—yes, even the
commonplace coconut-palm of every tropical coastland spelt
enchantment.

So it was in a dream that in 1907 I sailed for the Far East. When
at last the ship tied up at Tanjong Paka I humped a rucksack,
stepped ashore, and set off. I was going for a hitch-hike and did
not intend to be back that night. I took the tram in to Singapore,
asked the way to Woodlands, on the other side of the island
(there was no causeway in those days, or dockyard either), and
started down the Tanglyn Road, still in a dream. I must have
been in a dream, or perhaps even a swoon, because I remember

so few of the plants I saw. The vegetation recalled some of my favourite pictures in Schimper, and also some large photographs my father had brought back from Ceylon in 1882, which always fascinated me; but I do not remember the plants.... In due course, having slept a night by the Bukit Tima road, I returned to the ship. That was my night out: fireflies and bullfrogs.

Though I had early fallen under the spell of the tropics, I was no youthful prodigy. On this occasion I made no original observations, nor did I collect and preserve any undescribed plants—in fact, any plants at all. I just wanted to steep myself in an atmosphere, to revel in the scents, and to see with my own eyes all the exuberance of life that the warmth, humidity, and equinoctial time-sequence of the tropics produces.

From Schimper I had graduated to Hooker's *Himalayan Journals*, Wallace's *Island Life*, Bates's *Naturalist on the Amazons*, Belt's *Naturalist in Nicaragua*, and other classics of biological exploration. Nevertheless at Cambridge I had allowed myself to be caught up by the Machine. There was only one god, and Tripos was his name. Text-books took the place of Adventures, which offered no quick dividends in marks; injections of concentrated facts replaced the musings of explorers. But when, having committed to memory the guts of a dogfish, the articulations of a lobster, the nerves of a man, and the bonded atoms of a hydrocarbon, I got only second-class honours I found myself somewhat off balance. (I feel it only fair to say, however, that I achieved this in two years instead of the usual three.)

However, if I had to answer questions as to *why* I continued in the profession of plant-hunting I should find it difficult now to give any one simple reason. Perhaps in the beginning, when I had the chance to change while still a novice, I felt ashamed to admit defeat so early in what I had always believed was my real line of work. I knew well enough that my first few journeys in search of plants had not been a rousing success; but I had set my hand to the plough, and though more than once I had qualms that I should never get into the front rank of botanical explorers, at other times I still felt that this was the one career for which I was somehow fitted. Consequently when a well-known gardener of the day confided to a friend that I had entirely the wrong temperament and should never make a successful plant-hunter—the remark was repeated to me—I was indignant. Deep down I had a certain confidence in myself. I had resigned my first job, as a schoolmaster in Shanghai—which, however, I regarded from the beginning merely as a means to an end—not only because it was uncongenial, but also because I disliked, and had no confidence in, my employers; but to walk out now on what I believed to be my vocation because of a poor start was unthinkable. I might have set myself a goal beyond my capacity, but when all was said and done I enjoyed reaching for it. In the last analysis I think that I continued as a plant-hunter, going on from year to year, as long as I felt that I could derive pleasure—the pleasure of fulfil-ment—and pride from it. In fact, the pleasure and the pride gradually increased—and this was as well, because presently it was too late to change. Habit is a very compelling force.

I do not wish to imply that plant-hunting, even if it is not exactly one long holiday, is ever dull routine. The events of the day, except for comparatively short spells during the rainy season, are, I think, definitely less predictable than what one might expect if one had to be at the office by 9.30 every morning; though not necessarily more instructive or exciting. They strike deeper emotionally, but their effect is more transient. The real stuff of life, the human contacts with their tragedies and comedies, somehow seem more remote to the traveller in far places than to the season-ticket holder, and so do the amenities of a certain standard of living. A routine life naturally appeals to a great many people; probably to most people. But I cut myself adrift from this anchorage, and set a course of my own, prepared to move with the shifting currents when I could make no headway against them; and soon a return to the old anchorage became impossible.

But the real reason why I stuck to plant-hunting still eludes me. It was not pure obstinacy; still less can it have been for material rewards. A preference for simplicity was, I believe, one factor; and when I recall all the moments of intense happiness that I have enjoyed, even in years of failure and disappointment, I can only suppose that some element of romance must also have lain behind it; the romance that I found so long ago in Schimper's pictures. Plant-hunting has always seemed to me a romantic occupation—and romance must be a part of life, or people would not cling to it so irrationally, even when the pursuit of it gives so much unease. For my part, no sooner was one journey finished, no sooner had I said to myself (as in the early years I did more than once), "Thank heaven *that's* over!" and assured myself,

One of the great rivers of Asia, as it storms its way down to the distant sea

The foot-long externally crimson internally green pitcher of a Malaysian pitcher-plant (Nepenthes reinwardtiana) growing in forest at Dulit, Sarawak

Photo P. M. Synge

A cultivated pitcher-plant (Nepenthes, garden hybrid), grown in a hanging basket for good drainage, with pitchers in various stages of development at tips of leaves

By courtesy of the Royal Botanic Gardens, Kew

"Never again," than all the troubles and difficulties fell away, were forgotten; the memorably happy hours glowed more brightly than they had ever done in reality, and I began to long for the hills again.

But where, in all these journeyings in the mountains of Southeast Asia, among tribesmen who spoke unintelligible languages, lay, exactly, the romance? I think very much in the untamed beauty of the landscape, in its form and colour, and also in the strong pull of untrodden ways—the ever-present hope that any day I might discover something—a flower, a mountain, a river or a lake—hitherto unknown; something new to science. There was always ample scope for such discovery. There was romance too in the deep silence—not an oppressive, menacing silence, but a profound tranquillity. And how marvellously blue—that celestial colour—the whole world was! Blue is at the very heart of romance, conceivably because it is at the top end of the spectrum; the two widest expanses the eye can embrace, sea and sky, are both blue. At sunset the short lilac dusk crept over the world, and the shadows ceased to lengthen before merging into the night; soon everything visible from the camp took on an indigo tinge. But by day distant ranges of hills are always blue, and so are jungle-filled valleys. The high-lying ice of glaciers had a blue gleam, the rolling rivers reflected the blue sky; alpine flowers like gentians, Meconopsis, and forget-me-nots were bluer than any flowers I had ever seen. As for the mountain lakes, usually they glittered like sapphires in their rough setting, though a few were deep and green and cold as jade.

Colour there always was, even in winter, when snow wrapped the hills in a white shroud, and the babble of brooks ceased. In the frozen silence the peaks looked like carved silver; the dark aisles of the forest glowed with the scarlet berries of leafless shrubs.

Late autumn and early winter are the best times to realize the structure of a landscape, because the weather is generally fine, and one can see both the most distant hills and the fantastic sculpturing of the nearest ranges. Time, and power in many forms, have combined to forge this landscape; and the power is still there, even if dormant, to refashion it. The visible rocks were thrust up from deep down in the crust of the earth, where they had lain plastic since the beginning of time. At last they solidified in crystalline form, or flowed and set like molten iron when the pressure was released. Yet, hard as they were, they were not so hard that wind and water, in the millennia to come, could not erode and carve them into towers and troughs and spires and gorges. The debris went to make soil; and life, humble to begin with, but becoming more advanced as the soil grew richer and deeper, spread like a film over them. Then small flowering-plants arrived: by wind-borne seeds, from seeds carried in the crops of birds, or in mud sticking to their feet, or among the stalks they plucked to build their nests. So grass and sedge and pea-flowered plants and dandelions sprang up, until gradually the rocks became overgrown, adding more colour to the scene.

But it is not enough that romance lies behind the birth and growth of the landscape, and the mantle of plants which clothes it. The happy traveller must seek to convey some of that romance to others who have not had the good fortune to enjoy it; and what better means can there be of doing just that, than by introducing the plants which grow in these remote places into English gardens? One can describe and show pictures of sights seen in the far hills, but nothing is half so convincing as seeing the flowers which actually grow there; seeing them, not as specimens in a museum, but as living, breathing plants. Naturally many of them, shrubs and trees especially, will take years to reach flowering age, but no matter. To-day we gaze with delight and awe on horse-chestnuts and giant redwoods growing in our parks—all of them introduced and planted by our forbears. They recall to our minds the romantic stories of their discovery, of the expeditions to collect seed, of the long slow journeys to England, and of the care devoted to their upbringing and getting them established.

And so, too, will future generations look with pleasure, not unmixed with awe, on the veteran big-leafed rhododendron-trees discovered in China; on the dawn redwoods (Metasequoia), and on many other trees, now still young, introduced only in the twentieth century. One can hardly look at an English oak without remembering that barely 150 years ago they were the bulwarks that saved England from invasion. In those days it was a patriotic act to plant an acorn where a tree would grow, to launch yet another frigate or ship of the line with which to beat the enemy. If there are sermons in stones, no less certain is it that there are poems in trees.

Several people have asked me, "How did you begin?" A very natural question; yet I always find it slightly embarrassing, because as I have said, I am not certain of the answer. After all, how *did* I begin? Or how does any plant-hunter begin?

Before I actually became a plant-hunter I had travelled by junk and on foot across the breadth of China, from the coast to the edge of the world. This was the result of a letter from an American zoologist, Mr Malcolm P. Anderson, inviting me to accompany him on a journey through the mountainous provinces of Hupeh, Shensi, Kansu, and Szechwan, to collect birds and mammals. Though Anderson was a stranger to me, we had a mutual friend in Oldfield Thomas, then Keeper of Zoology at the British Museum (Natural History), in London, and a distinguished scientist; Anderson had been studying under him, and it was entirely owing to Oldfield Thomas that I received this very unexpected and welcome invitation. I accepted by return, lest Anderson change his mind. At the same time I realized that I should have to ask my employers in Shanghai to release me from my contract, which had still a year to run—and this, after some hesitation, they rather grudgingly did. (Presumably they did not find me indispensable, but less than generously, they stuck to the whole of my small provident fund as a *quid pro quo*.) I confessed to Anderson that my qualifications for collecting animals were slender, as I was really a student of botany—though I had as a matter of fact 'done' a course in zoology too; I also told him that though I had lived in Shanghai for two years, I did not, as he seemed to hope, speak Chinese.

In no way discouraged by these shortcomings, he kept in touch with me, though I grew impatient as the weeks passed. However, in due course he reached Shanghai, where he spent a fortnight making all necessary preparations. Dr Jack Smith, a medical missionary who was convalescing after a long illness, joined Anderson as interpreter; thus the party was complete, and we left Shanghai in September 1909.

A year later, after an interesting journey, and some experience which was later to stand me in good stead, I was back in Shanghai, where I returned temporarily to my old job. Malcolm Anderson stayed on in western China to continue his zoological work. (He was killed by a falling tree during the First World War, while logging in the United States. He was then barely forty.) Jack Smith went off as interpreter with H. F. Wallace, the distinguished Scottish artist and big-game hunter, who had come to China to hunt the golden takin. Smith was invaluable on any expedition, not only for his medical skill and knowledge of Chinese, and his great popularity with the people everywhere, but also for his charm, tact, and human kindness to everybody. How long would I, now itching to go on another expedition, have to remain in Shanghai, I wondered?

And then suddenly, out of the blue, came a second letter from a stranger, asking me if I would like to go on a one-man expedition; this time it *was* to be plant-hunting!

The letter was from Arthur K. Bulley, a cotton-broker of Liverpool, who lived at Neston, in Cheshire, close to the sands of Dee, and died in 1942. Bulley, I learnt, was a connoisseur of alpine plants, an enthusiastic gardener, founder of the nursery firm of Bees, Ltd, and a prominent Socialist. After the war he found himself a near-millionaire—his only real grievance in life, I believe! He had recently employed George Forrest to collect for him in Yunnan, but Forrest had now gone over to J. C. Williams, of Caerhays Castle, in Cornwall, and Bulley invited me to take his place and carry on where Forrest had left off. The Regius Professor of Botany at Edinburgh, Sir Isaac Bayley Balfour, was the link in this case—he was an old friend of my father.

I replied at once, accepting the offer, though this time I kept quiet about my qualifications—or lack of them—for the job. Had I not recently crossed China on foot? Was I not a fully fledged botanist? At least I had a university degree in botany,[1] which amounted to almost the same thing! Didn't it?

So towards the end of the year I once more gave my employers notice, and a month later left Shanghai for the second time, never to return. I had achieved my heart's desire. I had become a plant-hunter.

However, as I was quickly to learn, I was not quite so well-equipped for the profession of plant-hunting as I had imagined. The fact is that for the particular end in view an academic education and a university degree (which I achieved, academically, five years later by keeping another term) were of far less use to me than a knowledge of plants grown in the garden would have been. I had really to start at the beginning, but my education was continuous; I learnt as much when on home leave from

---

[1] Actually, I hadn't!—not having spent my full three years at Cambridge. But I had passed my tripos with honours at the end of two years instead of the usual three.

my gardening friends, particularly from Sir Frederick Stern and Mr Lionel de Rothschild, as I did when at work in the field.

That, I think, is perhaps one reason why I find it embarrassing to be asked how I became a plant-hunter. Somehow it has been made to sound faintly parasitic. But I have tried to explain how it came about. There was my strong original impulse, followed by an unusual mixture of chance and good luck. 'Love from a stranger'—*that* can come only once in a lifetime—but a letter from a stranger came to me twice in three years! I seized the chance each time—and luck, with a little help, did the rest. Thus Bulley's letter decided my life (with two long breaks) for the next forty-five years.

Forty-five years' holiday? Or forty-five years' 'hard'?

Looking back on it, I'm not sure which. But—well, yes, both.

· 2 ·

Little Pitchers

DURING my uncongenial time of schoolmastering in Shanghai I did not spend my two summer holidays— 'hot-weather leave'—cooling off in Japan, as all sensible people do. Instead I went south to the equator, the first time to Java, the second to Borneo, there to revel in the tropical scenes which the books of Schimper and Wallace had filled with romance for me. Yet in these two journeys, though I saw and recorded many of the most typical and common eastern tropical plants—swamp-palms, mangrove, giant bamboo, and others— there were many equally common, but none the less striking for that, which I did not even see. I do not recall noticing many epiphytic orchids other than the largest of them all (Grammatophyllum), or the giant arum (Amorphophallus), or the talipot-palm (Corypha), or any of the huge lianas I had read about.

More surprisingly, I saw no pitcher-plants; at least, I have no recollection of seeing any, not even in the magnificent tropical garden of Buitenzorg (now Bogor) in Java. In fact, I had spent a good many years in the East before I first saw pitcher-plants growing wild on Singapore island, and even longer before I found one for myself in Assam. But as I was seldom in the tropics (since I was collecting temperate plants), perhaps this was not so surprising after all.

Naturally, it is the Assamese pitcher-plant of which I have the clearest recollection; not only because it was the one I saw most recently, but also because I derived such great pleasure from finding it myself. Moreover, it is associated in my mind with an unusual episode. By that time, however, exploring for plants had long since become my profession.

The distribution of the genus Nepenthes—pitcher-plants—had already aroused my curiosity, for its pattern is so bizarre as to be whimsical. Whenever I was in the tropics, even for a few days, I kept a look-out for these strange plants which range so far afield, yet only occur as widely sundered pinpoints in far vaster areas of non-occurrence. Apart from the sixty or seventy known species, was it not possible to find a *new* species? After all, I had been finding a good many new temperate plants in the mountains of South-east Asia; why not a new pitcher-plant?

But perhaps that might be more difficult. One must not forget that a plant so peculiar will be noticed and singled out by the most primitive of mankind, and endowed with near-magic properties, curative or aphrodisiac. The more strange-looking the plant, the more potent its supposed effects; the uneducated mind perceives fanciful analogies where the educated mind looks for causes. Thus it is certain that many pitcher-plants, especially those which grow in the coastal foothills, or on the plains, have been known from time immemorial. However, I had penetrated to glens which were scarcely known even to the natives of these parts; indeed, it would be true to say that often there *were* no natives. For the moment I was primitive man, seeking know-ledge; and some of these places appeared well-suited to pitcher-plants.

But appearances can be very deceptive. If one vital substance is lacking—no more than a trace element perhaps—plants which need just that cannot grow; or it may be a condition which is lacking—humidity at the significant time, or temperature; or all conditions may be well-suited to the plant, and no doubt it could settle in a certain region and make a home for itself. But suppose it never got there!

Whatever the reason, neither in farthest Burma nor in wildest Assam did I ever find a pitcher-plant, although everything seemed to make this a desirable residential area, until I went with a friend to Jaintiapur, which is an ancient city in eastern India.

Before telling the simple story of finding the Khasi pitcher-plant—no new species this, but one known to western botanists for a long time—I will say a little more about their distribution.

Within the enormous area they so inadequately cover—nine thousand or ten thousand miles from east to west—several out-liers occur. These outliers, as botanists call species which are isolated from the common herd of kith and kin, are spread hap-hazard round the periphery of the area: thus there is one in

Madagascar, though none in tropical East Africa; one in the Seychelles; one in Ceylon (none in South India); one in the Khasi hills, in Assam, but none in the tropical hills and swamps of Bengal; and one in New Caledonia far out in the Pacific Ocean. There is likewise one in Siam, though none in Burma; one in Annam, and one in south-east China. This last, unlike the others mentioned, is widespread over much of South-east Asia, so that its being an outlier on the China coast also is of no special significance. That is merely its farthest station north.

The outliers apart, most of the sixty or seventy species are well distributed over Malaya, Indonesia, the Philippines, New Guinea, and north-eastern Queensland. They are most numerous in Borneo (twenty to twenty-five species), which is perhaps their centre of distribution and starting-point.

They seem to have a predilection for islands; and since isolated tropical mountain-tops, so far as the distribution of plants is concerned, behave like islands, we find them growing freely on such mountains, notably on the great peak of Kinabalu, in North Borneo.

The distribution of Nepenthes to-day hardly suggests that the Himalayan glaciation had any serious effect on them, though one cannot be certain of that. The retreat of the ice may at least have enabled a few species to push northward from the congested equatorial zone into the empty spaces freed by the ice.

How they reached such remote spots as New Caledonia and Madagascar is something of a puzzle. If a few more species were to be discovered—say one or two in tropical East Africa, others on the west side of India, or in peninsular Burma—their distribution would cease to be quite so remarkable; or if a few fossil species could be discovered it might help. So far, no leaf impressions have been found in the rocks; or at least none have been recognized.

In pre-glacial times, perhaps as recently as a quarter of a million years ago, land and sea, particularly in South-east Asia, were not arranged quite as they are to-day; some of the land was sea, some of the sea was land. But how much? What seems certain is that a vast peninsula embracing Sumatra, Java, and Borneo continued south-eastward from modern Siam and Malaya, reaching almost to New Guinea and Australia on the one hand, and to the Philippines on the other. This is the heart of the pitcher-plant country to-day, and may well have been so then.

Like orchids, pitcher-plants have very small seeds, produced in prodigious numbers and easily wind-borne over great distances. Unlike the seeds of orchids, however, their seeds germinate readily, and quickly give rise to young plants. The majority of them are, or can be, epiphytic, which gives them a good chance of survival on drifting tree-trunks or floating masses of vegetation.

If, then, the great Indonesian peninsula, of almost continental size, was rich in Nepenthes, it is quite possible that these plants were widely dispersed round the coasts of South-east Asia by oceanic and atmospheric currents alone, and thence to some of the islands of the Indian Ocean. At that time, with the ice-age looming over the horizon and fluctuations of climate increasing, it is probable that many strong marine currents prevailed and that families like the pitcher-plants and orchids were widely distributed by such natural means. Changes of climate must also have occurred, wiping out species here, leaving survivors as outliers there. But what is it that limits their spread?

And so to Assam, and my solitary pitcher-plant. From the motor-road at Jaintiapur we were ferried by dug-out across the shallow swamps to the foot of the cliff. Above us lay the Khasi plateau. We climbed two thousand feet by the old stone-paved track, up long flights of rough steps. A hundred generations of coolies had toiled barefooted up and down between the plains and the plateau; but no wheeled traffic had ever passed this way —not even the mobile Chinese wheelbarrow. At dusk we found shelter in the empty, echoing rest-house; far below, the last light glimmered on the wet paddy-fields. I had read that the Khasi pitcher-plant grew hereabouts, and had it not been already dark, I would have gone straightway in search of it; as it was, I looked forward eagerly to finding it next day.

And in the morning, within half a mile of the bungalow, find it I did. It grew among scattered bushes on a low rock, half scrambling up among the tangle of vegetation, half sprawling in a heap. The long, rigid, orchid-like stems grew in every direction, and from under the mass peeped scores of rotten, cracked, and mildewed pitchers; but all round the edge of the thicket young stems, clothed with fresh leaves and new apple-green pitchers, were coming up. There were a score or more of separate plants, altogether forming a considerable colony.

It is not the flowers but the pitchers which immediately catch the eye. Anyway the flowers were long since over, though the clubs which had borne them were still conspicuous. The pitchers develop from the *leaves*, and there were pitchers in every stage of growth, from a tiny green disc at the apex of a leaf to a full-sized rosy-cheeked pitcher dangling at the end of a thread eighteen inches long. Except for the pitcher and its supporting thread, the leaf looks like hundreds of other leaves.

Each pitcher begins as a minute disc, like a thin green button (at the end of a short thread), which appears as soon as the midrib has grown on independently beyond the tip of the young leaf. Gradually the disc inflates itself, swelling slowly like a pale-green toy balloon; when it has reached a diameter of about a quarter of an inch it begins to grow longer rather than broader, eventually assuming a pitcher-shape, about six inches long by two across when fully grown. At this stage it has a sealed lid. Meanwhile the suspending thread also grows rapidly, and, being sensitive to contact, may take a turn round any convenient support, thus helping to carry the weight of the mature pitcher, which must otherwise rest on the ground. (Very often it does.) Finally the lid separates about three-quarters of the way round, leaving a hinge, and opens.

The lip of the finished pitcher is smooth, and curved inward like the railings which surround a prohibited area—the difference being that here the inquisitive are encouraged to *enter* the pitcher! In fact, the involuted rim, like the mouth of a lobster-pot, is designed to *keep* creatures in—not to prevent their entering. The inner surface of the pitcher is also smooth, and slippery; it is freckled with glands, visible to the naked eye as tiny black dots. Some of these glands secrete honey, which attracts insects and spiders; others, rather different and placed down near the base, secrete a juice which digests organic matter. These secretions, together with clear water, collect at the bottom of the pitcher, sometimes to a depth of an inch or two. The liquid has a slightly salty flavour.

Into this Pool of Siloam honey-loving creatures slither while trying to obtain free board and lodging; unable to swim or to climb out, they are soon drowned. When they are dead their soft parts are quickly digested and absorbed.

That, in a nutshell, is the whole works: the fantastic pitchers, each an open mouth and a ravenous stomach; the enticing sweetness secreted by the pitcher wall; the water-trap below; the deadly active juices. Once lured into the pitcher, escape is impossible. The trap is very efficient. It is not just a curiosity of nature; it is a living, working organism. The green leaves function in the ordinary way, and manufacture carbohydrates, while the highly specialized pitchers ensure a supply of nitrogen for the manufacture of proteins. (Nitrates are usually absent from the sphagnum, or peaty marshes, in which pitcher-plants grow.)

I found that the fully grown pitchers held a festering mass of creatures, alive and dead, but especially dead. The stink was frightful. Among them it was easy to recognize ants, beetles, flies of several kinds, crickets, grasshoppers, spiders, small butterflies, and even caterpillars and other larvae. Every pitcher, each a most delicately wrought, beautifully tinted piece of apparatus, eventually becomes an unpleasantly smelly funeral urn.

It was early November when I found the pitchers, and they were then up to one-third full of insect food, on which the plants were drawing for their nitrogen ration. But Sir Joseph Hooker, one of the most renowned botanists of the nineteenth century, had a different experience. When he was collecting at Amwee in the Jyntea hills in 1850 he found this same pitcher-plant, and in his famous *Himalayan Journals* we read, "Its pitchers seldom contain insects in the wild state." This was in September. He goes on to say that he cannot suggest what use the pitchers are to the plant! Coming from so brilliant a botanist, this is surprising. On the other hand, J. M. Macfarlane, an authority on the genus, writes that "all travellers agree in describing the abundance of insect remains in the pitchers," and later, "it seems largely true that running insects, such as ants and cockroaches, form the principal prey of the group."

I have written that the finding of the Khasi pitcher-plant was marked by an unusual episode. After collecting specimens I returned to the rest-house to examine my prize. It was a warm, sunny day, and everything seemed to be in a comfortable doze. I noticed that the dirty ceiling-cloth which hung beneath the steep thatched roof sagged badly; but there was no breeze to make it flap. I sat at the table beneath, and spread out my plants. Suddenly pandemonium broke loose just over my head, and I leapt to my feet.

The ceiling-cloth was being violently shaken, as some heavy weight charged wildly up and down, making a terrific to-do, though there was no recognizable noise, animal or other—just upheaval and these amorphous and anonymous sounds. The whole roof seemed to shake, and the cloth, heaving now here, now there, threatened to collapse altogether; the ragged edges fluttered awkwardly, and every moment I expected a great rent to appear and something to drop through into the room. But the cloth was stronger than it looked; it held, in spite of the violent agitation. By this time I had an idea of what the intruder might be. Seizing a strong cane walking-stick I had recently cut, I jumped on to the table and lashed at the unseen object which was still cavorting round; by its shape it could only be a snake—but how to hit its head!

I lashed at it through the limp cloth till the writhing motion began to subside; the blows must have hurt. If I could only find the creature's head I might kill it quickly; but by now my arm was so tired that I could hardly lift it. I got down from the table and went into the next room to fetch a gun; on my return I saw a curious sight. The head of a large snake just showed, hanging over the edge of the ceiling-cloth, where it sagged between two fixed points. It looked the picture of misery, and appeared to be so thoroughly exhausted—with mouth open and staring eyes— that for a moment I felt a pang of remorse. It was probably a rat snake, and it was clear now that the original rumpus had been caused by its pouncing on a victim. The inhabitants of a thatch roof in an Indian bungalow are many and varied, and possibly the snake met with something larger than a rat; it may even have encountered its match and failed to kill. But of these things I could not be sure.

I am not unduly sentimental about wild animals; but neither do I kill them on principle, or for lack of it. And when the snake withdrew from sight, back to some dark and secret corner of the roof where it could nurse its aches, I let it go at that. But the snake's violence and the peacefully predatory pitcher-plant remain as one in my memory.

In south-western Australia grows a strange plant whose name is Cephalotus. If you happened to find it out of flower you would say without hesitation, and rightly, that it was a pitcher-plant, for the leaves develop pitchers from the end of the midrib in exactly the same way as Nepenthes, from which these pitchers cannot be distinguished (outwardly at any rate). Pitcher-plant it is, though no Nepenthes.

Yet in its geographical setting it could be regarded as just another outlying Nepenthes. Nor would a Nepenthes be out of place here, except that it is rather far beyond the equatorial zone. The two great areas of concentration of Nepenthes are the Indonesian and Austronesian archipelagos—that is to say, Sumatra, Java, and Borneo, with an extension into the mainland of Asia, particularly Malaya, on the one hand, and New Guinea, the Philippines, and north-east Australia on the other. An outlier of the Austronesian archipelago in south-western Australia is of course no more anomalous than is an outlier of the Indonesian archipelago in Madagascar; at least it is not more than half as far distant! But Cephalotus is not an outlier of Nepenthes; nor even a near relation. It is an outsider.

It would seem that if nature, having made pitcher-plants, was dissatisfied with her work and broke the mould, she relented and produced Mark II; unless, of course, it was the other way about, and she made Cephalotus first, as an experimental type! If so she was pleased with her handiwork, for Mark II Nepenthes, the true pitcher-plant, had a tremendous vogue. But on the evidence it seems more likely that both plants arose independently. And that is curious.

· 3 ·

Magnolia Mixture

WE speak of flowering-trees as though there were other trees which do not flower. Gardeners, who are never pedants, also speak of flowering-trees when they mean trees with obvious and conspicuous flowers, as opposed to others —in fact, the majority—which have small, dull, or trivial flowers.

This rough classification into flowering- and non-flowering-trees corresponds with our own experience. In our youth we fail to notice insignificant flowers. What we call flowering-trees are those generally grown for the sake of their flowers alone, while so-called non-flowering-trees are grown for their foliage, shape, or some other quality. Botanists know quite well what the layman means when he speaks of flowering-trees, and accept the implied fallacy with resignation. A botanist may observe caustically that non-flowering-trees went out with the Coal Measures some 220 million years ago, but he isn't really misled.

In Britain we don't happen to have many native 'flowering-trees'; even oak, lime, and elm scarcely qualify. Undoubtedly those which open their flower-buds before they expand their leaves come nearest the definition. But the service-tree and haw-thorn also qualify, though the flowers open *after* the leaves. If it be insisted that pussy-willows are shrubs and not trees they hardly deserve to be disqualified for that.

The best-loved and the most handsome flowering-tree in England is the horse-chestnut, even though leaves and flowers emerge from the same bud and open at the same time. The white horse-chestnut was introduced into this country from the Balkans in the early years of the reign of Queen Elizabeth I, and after more than four centuries has become so familiar as to be commonly looked upon as a native tree. We have, in fact, taken it to our hearts, reserved a day in the calendar—Chestnut

Sunday—to pay homage to it as though it were a saint, and use its seeds in a game which has become a cult with a ritual of its own among small country boys. But as a matter of fact it is barely naturalized. Horse-chestnuts are usually planted.

Perhaps the finest flowering-trees in the world are the deciduous magnolias, particularly those which flower before the leaves unfurl—alien to England and to Europe, but cultivated for their splendid flowers wherever they can be grown. In the warmer part of the continent, and in southern and western Britain, these magnolias are quite at home; which is as it should be, since they are the dispossessed.

Before the ice-age turned central Europe into a vast tundra, magnolias—or trees closely related to them—were common in the Pliocene forests a million years ago, as is proved by the frequency with which their fossil remains are found. At all events, several species have settled down complacently in Europe, though their assisted passages back to their lost homeland have not been without incident.

Of these deciduous magnolias one, whose ancestors had probably never seen Europe before, was first recorded by the Scottish plant-hunter George Forrest, who discovered it in south-west China in 1917. It seems doubtful whether Forrest himself ever saw the tree, at any rate in flower. Probably specimens were brought to him by his Chinese collectors. However that may be, Forrest described it as a tall, deciduous tree, up to eighty feet high, with bright rose-pink flowers opening before the leaves. Thus it competed for pride of place with *Magnolia campbellii* itself, hitherto regarded as unique.

When news of this fabulous tree reached England (in a letter from Forrest) a subdued but continuous hum of applause could be heard in horticultural circles. But at that time the First World War was raging, and nobody had time to linger over these delights.

The war ended, and peace broke out—though hardly a world peace.

In 1919, when Forrest's magnolia, raised from seed, had reached the tender age of one year, Farrer visited North Burma. At the same time Forrest was again in Yunnan, and while his collectors were making their way westward towards Burma, Farrer himself was approaching the Burma–China frontier from the west, and in roughly the same latitude.

It was hereabouts that Forrest's magnolia had been found two years earlier; and in due course Farrer too found it in the dense forest. He confirmed Forrest's description of it—in even more extravagant terms—the flowers "literally as big as 'tay-kettles,' very fragrant and solid and abundant in every shade from pure white to deep and rather magenta-rose." It is certain that Farrer saw the tree with his own eyes and he may have known all that there was to be known about it before he left England. When two men, so different in many ways, but alike in both being first-class observers and knowledgeable about plants, gave an almost identical report there was no room for doubt that here grew a magnificent flowering tree. A scientific description by Sir William Wright Smith, based on Forrest's fruiting and flowering specimens, but citing Farrer's also, was published in *Notes from the Royal Botanic Garden, Edinburgh*, Vol. 12: pp. 213–215 (1920). As the beaked carpels of Forrest's fruiting material were unlike those of other magnolias, it was named *Magnolia rostrata*. Nothing remained except to await its flowering in England.

In those halcyon days, which were the golden age of English gardening, the late Lionel de Rothschild used to give lunch-parties to gardening friends at New Court, in the City; and when I was in England I was sometimes invited. They were delightful functions—Lionel de Rothschild's hospitality was proverbial, and I met here men distinguished in the public service, in business, in science and art, who were also reckoned among the greatest gardeners in the country.

I remember particularly one such party at which eight or ten guests were present—I think it was the first I ever attended. Conversation flowed easily, touching lightly on topics of the day, until our host introduced the subject which interested everybody—that is to say, gardening.

Suddenly the man sitting on my right—I need not mention his name—leant across the table, and in a sort of wheezy whisper, asked his opposite neighbour, "How many seeds of *M. rostrata* have you raised?" (So fresh consignments of seed had been distributed.)

"Up to last month, three," came the rather wary reply. "And you?"

The first speaker's face fell. Perhaps he regretted having asked the question as he replied, still in the same wheezy half-whisper, "Two, but ..."

I did not hear the reason why his score was only two, for at that moment some one asked me if I had seen *M. rostrata* in North Burma, whence I had recently returned.

"Not in flower," I replied cautiously.

At our end of the table I noticed the conversation was running down. Somebody had stopped short when launching into an involved story about some cherry-trees imported from a Yokohama nurseryman. All ears seemed to be tuned in to the magnolia metre band. A hush had fallen on the company as though the Grand Lama had just pronounced the sacred words, "Om mani padme hum." However, it was the sacred words *M. rostrata* which had been pronounced as a sort of benediction, and for the first time I realized that the plant had been canonized during its lifetime.

Conversation began again. I remembered that some years previously in the rain forest of North Burma I had picked up large beaked cones lying on a steep slope, and had wondered what they were. I was suffering badly from malaria at the time, and had never followed up the clue thus offered. Little did I realize that they belonged to an unknown species of magnolia. I must have stood beneath *M. rostrata* several times, and had I been more perspicacious I might have had a good share in the discovery of this tiresome tree.

At the time of which I write—that short but dazzling horticultural epoch between two world wars—gardeners were planning and planting the parks and gardens of Britain for the next hundred years— at any rate they were preparing a wealth of material for that purpose. Many of them were willing, if necessary, to wait a quarter of a century for a first sight of *M. rostrata*. They believed that just to see its great rosy-pink flowers and giant leaves would justify a lifelong wait. Anyway, they were planting for the future as their fathers had done before them.

Shortly after that lunch-party I went abroad again.

Forrest and Farrer reported what they saw, or what they thought they saw; and the description of the plant issued from the Edinburgh Botanic Garden possessed for horticulturists all the authority of a papal bull. It must have pleased the two collectors.

Yet, before long a query arose. Did the seeds from which plants were being raised come from the same trees as those with the splendid flowers? Authority was challenged by authority. What had happened? Mr J. E. Dandy, a taxonomist of repute, now Keeper of Botany at the British Museum (Natural History), in London, and an expert on magnolias, presently examined all the available material referred to *M. rostrata*. No sooner had he done so than he perceived that some one had blundered. Possibly a mistake had been made in the field, which in turn led to a mistake in the herbarium, and in the description of *M. rostrata*; and so on in ever-widening circles of error. (In fact, every generation of botanists seems to spend half its time correcting the mistakes and omissions of the previous generation.) Dandy recognized in the leaves and cones before him (just as Professor Sir William Wright Smith had done) a strikingly distinct species. But he pointed out that it was quite impossible for it to have precocious flowers—as the term is; they could only come out *after* the leaves. This fact had been overlooked, and the description of the tree, stating that it flowered while still leafless, was a mistake. Misled by the accompanying but unattached flower specimens, Wright Smith, who had been the first to examine the herbarium specimens, had certainly gone astray.

The flower-buds of a winter-flowering magnolia like *M. campbellii*, which opens in February, are completed the previous autumn, and rest throughout the winter; the leaf-buds are formed much later, and open as soon as they are fully developed. *M. rostrata* clearly belongs to a different group. Its terminal flower-buds lag far behind its leaf-buds, not opening till the leaves are fully expanded.

As for the unattached flowers, alleged to be those of *M. rostrata*, Dandy detected something wrong here too: they didn't match the accompanying leaf-branchlets, he said, and must belong to those of some other species, probably *M. campbellii*.

Experts, like laymen, do make mistakes, only not so often. When they do they are the more grievous, and it takes longer to correct them, and establish the truth. This magnolia myth persisted for some time after it had been exploded. When the facts became known, nine-year-old plants of *M. rostrata* were already available in British gardens. But nothing short of actual flowering-plants would convince the sceptics. It must have been about 1927, that the first whisper of doubt stole round the horticultural world, and was quickly and painlessly put away like an unwanted kitten. But it left its mark, and from then onward every man who had raised a seedling of the magnolia had a millstone of uncertainty slung round his neck. What, he was asking himself, *is Magnolia rostrata*?

If Dandy was right (as in fact he was) it followed that Forrest and his native collectors had confused two species in the jungle —*M. campbellii* in flower about February, with *M. rostrata* in leaf a month or two later. As a matter of fact, up to this time, although a few flowers of the real *M. rostrata* had been collected, they were ignored; all flowers which had passed for that species really belonged to *M. campbellii*. I can vouch for it that it would be easy to confuse them in the forest, since the two trees look very similar without their leaves, and though they overlap in North Burma, one never sees them in flower together. While Forrest and possibly Farrer had confused two species, I had not even seen *M. rostrata*, though I had idly picked up the big beaked cones.

Thus there was nothing very remarkable in a collector's having made a mistake in the field, however experienced he might be. That mistake was endorsed in the herbarium! But botanists in the herbarium are no more immune from mistakes than are collectors in the field. This possibly accounted for the reluctance of interested gardeners to give up hope. They were not amused, and obviously they *wanted* to believe in the magnolia of their dreams. They dug their heels in. The fact that by this time young plants had proved tender, even in the mildest districts, did not discourage them. Some day magnolia the magnificent would flower, and then its detractors would see! Forrest, confident in himself, did not retract.

I have said that *M. rostrata* and *M. campbellii* meet in North Burma; but that is only half the truth. In fact, they overlap by several hundred miles. Exactly ten years after the first recorded sight of *M. rostrata* I was exploring the gorge of the Tsangpo, in Tibet, where the great river rounds the snow peak of Namcha Barwa. One day I saw leafless magnolias on the lower slopes of the mountain, and picked up beneath them the dead leaves and cones of *M. rostrata*. This was in December, and, though I did not see it in flower, there was no doubt about the identification. The discovery of *M. rostrata* in the Tsangpo gorge extended its range two hundred or three hundred miles to the north-west of its first-known base—that is to say, it definitely established its presence on the main Himalayan range itself. It does not, however, extend so far west as Sikkim, or even Bhutan, which is the unchallenged preserve of *M. campbellii*. As *Magnolia campbellii* subsp. *mollicomata*—or *Magnolia mollicomata* as it is often called—the latter extends eastward as far as Yunnan, so that the two species really occupy almost the same territory. So far do they overlap.

The picture was now becoming clearer. But before *M. rostrata* flowered in Britain I became mildly involved in its fortunes again.

A few years after I had found *M. rostrata* in the Assam Himalaya I was collecting in the Mishmi hills farther east—one of Griffith's early collecting grounds. One day I walked down a fairly steep ridge, the sheltered flank of which was covered with rain forest, while the exposed south slope had some years before been cleared of forest, and was now overgrown with coarse grass. There, almost plumb on the crest of the ridge, I noticed a small tree with very large leaves, undoubtedly a magnolia. It bore several fat, pointed terminal buds, two of which opened some time later. It was probably flowering for the first time. This ridge was an ideal situation from which to view and photograph the tree, as one had only to climb higher to look down on to it from above and assess the flowers at their true worth. (From beneath they were invisible, each being seated on a wide platform of leaves, something like an Elizabethan ruff.) When I visited it again later I was not prepared for such undistinguished flowers in a magnolia. They were rather small and white or off-white, not to be compared with those of *M. campbellii*, and did little or nothing to enhance the beauty of the foliage. Against the background of sky or forest *M. rostrata* (for it was that) had a certain dignity, but nothing more. Magnolias are grown for their flowers, not for their leaves; and these flowers (which besides being small were untidy) ill-matched the leaves. I did not collect seed.

Later, by which time English-raised plants were about twelve years old, my comments on the Mishmi-hills tree appeared in the gardening press, and later in a travel book, accompanied by a photograph of *M. rostrata* in bud. No doubt, even before I took a hand in its debunking, few believed that *M. rostrata* was the ravishing beauty to whom they had paid court before she was even a débutante. Cumulative evidence had silenced the diehards

who had been her advance publicity agents; and the thunder of
applause which had heralded her coming had now died away to
a querulous murmur of disenchantment. Yet, at that date, no one
had ever seen the flowers of *M. rostrata*; the tree did not flower
in this country till 1935.

Shortly after my sight of it in the Mishmi hills the late W. J.
Bean published Volume III of his *Trees and Shrubs hardy in
the British Isles*, a classic of its kind, and a monument of accurate observation; though it seemed to me stretching a point to call
M. rostrata even half-hardy, in spite of the fact that there were
trees growing in the open in the mildest parts of the country.
Bean was a dour Yorkshireman, kind and generous in word and
deed to all except the pretentious. In a last stand to save the
tottering reputation of the beaked magnolia he spoke well of it,
again noting its claims as a remarkable foliage-tree; in his kindly
way he rapped me over the knuckles for speaking ill of it. (I had
written that the flowers were dingy white, and that the large
leaves, far from being a passport to the Garden of Eden, would
need much protection from wind.)

When I thought of the rapture with which a name and description had been received in horticultural circles twelve years earlier,
the ecstasy which the germination of a single seed had caused, I
felt sad. The disillusion suffered by the few who were nursing
young trees must have been bitter.

But at least the tangle had been resolved. *M. campbellii* and
M. rostrata were now themselves, and no longer each other.
Henceforth confusion was at an end.

Nevertheless to-day I am inclined to relent a little, to modify
my verdict that the claims of *M. rostrata* to rare distinction were
completely bogus. The reason for this change of heart is not due
to love at first sight of any specimen in England, still less to the
tree I saw in Assam; indeed, I have not seen one tree in England
yet. It dates only from 1953, when on an expedition in North
Burma I observed *M. rostrata* flowering in quantity for the first
time; and, to be honest, some of the trees seen from above were
worth looking at, though I will not put it higher than that.

It was towards the end of May, a very wet month that year, at
an altitude of eight thousand feet. We were camped in the temperate forest, where this magnolia was one of the commonest
trees. From the ridge on which our camp was pitched we could
see dozens of them in flower, among maples, oaks, laurels, and

many other trees, some familiar by name, others not; but more than all, big-leafed rhododendrons. Had these also been in flower they would have put *M. rostrata* completely in the shade. But they too flower early, and except for one glorious tree covered with large spherical trusses of bright-yellow flowers, the big-leafed rhododendrons were already over. Higher up the mountain, but also long since over, *M. campbellii* appeared here and there, with whitebeam and massed rhododendrons in full bloom. The two magnolia species, growing at different levels, scarcely met here.

By November the ragged crumpled leaves of *M. rostrata*, now the colour of grubby brown paper, were being blown off by the wind. They never take on autumn colour, nor do they remain hanging on the trees, which are bare for about four months. The tall straight cones, sometimes with the scarlet seeds peeping out from the gaping carpels, are conspicuous for their habit of standing boldly erect like candles on a Christmas-tree.

Now that it is no longer half something else one can discuss *M. rostrata* objectively. We hear very little about it in England to-day, though it has been in cultivation for forty years. The reason is not that we have failed to recognize its merits, but simply that it is neither very beautiful nor very hardy, and so not much sought after. But as I saw it on that very wet May 14, flowering in hundreds, scattered over the steep, thickly forested slope, I thought it worth looking at twice.

If I were conducting world tours to see the most magnificent flowering-trees at their finest hour, in their own homelands, I would not hesitate to include magnolias on the agenda. But it would not be *M. rostrata* in Burma. Rather would I shepherd travellers to the valleys above Gangtok in the Sikkim Himalaya, and there, in the bleak weather of February, show them *M. campbellii*. This confusing, though lovely, tree in Sikkim is usually white-flowered—at least in some valleys—more rarely pink. My tourists would gaze down in wonder on the dark forest, lit by thousands of milk-white glowing cups, hung like beacons in the bare trees, and be silent.

·4·

Blue Poppies

IN 1848 the first blue poppy flowered in England. To most people to-day a blue poppy means simply *Meconopsis baileyi*, which made its bow to the public in the year 1926, and is in any case incorrectly named—its full style and title is *Meconopsis betonicifolia baileyi*. But this was not the Meconopsis which flowered under glass at Kew over a hundred years ago; that was *M. simplicifolia*, a very different plant, though it too came from Tibet, or at least from high up in the Himalayas.

How, then, has it happened that this newcomer has stolen all the thunder, and become, to the general public at least, *the* blue poppy, as though there were no other in existence? What is the history of this upstart? Not only has the public acclaimed it as the one and only blue poppy, but in some nurserymen's catalogues it is still accorded the status of a new plant, usually under the incorrect name of *Meconopsis baileyi*—for a name once openly bestowed on a popular plant sticks like a bad habit.

It may help us in answering these questions, and in getting the facts sorted out from the half-truths, if we start with the genus Meconopsis as a whole. That will put everything into perspective.

Except for the Welsh Poppy (*Meconopsis cambrica*), all species of this genus are natives of Sino-Himalaya, a name given to the compact mountainous region which stretches from Kashmir and the plateau of Tibet through northernmost Burma into western China, embracing the Himalayas on the way.

It is reasonable to suppose that *M. cambrica*, an outlier in the far north-west, must be a survivor from the ice-age; and if that is so we may infer that in pre-glacial times the genus possibly spread right across Europe and northern Asia. The occurrence of *Meconopsis torquata* on the plateau of Tibet, not far from

Lhasa, and of a second species (and that one of the most wide-spread), *Meconopsis horridula*, at very high altitudes in Tibet, supports this conclusion. So does the occurrence of an outlier, *Meconopsis neglecta*, as far west as Chitral. Further, there is a plant in California called *Stylomecon heterophylla* which was for many years regarded as a species of Meconopsis under the name of *Meconopsis heterophylla*; this too suggests that the genus may originally—before the polar ice-cap forced the flora southward —have had a circumpolar distribution.

On the American continent plants escaping southward met with no obstacles on the way; hence, perhaps, the appearance of primulas in Patagonia. But no species of Meconopsis has survived in the Rockies, nor for that matter in Japan, to support the theory of a circumpolar distribution for that genus—which is a warning to us not to jump to conclusions. In Europe, how-ever, it is well known that two great barriers lay directly across the escape route—the Alps and the Mediterranean Sea. The trapped refugees suffered calamitous losses as a result. But, apparently by a lucky chance, *M. cambrica* escaped.

We need not then trouble to search for Meconopsis anywhere outside Sino-Himalaya; though if anyone announced to-morrow that he had discovered a Meconopsis in some obscure corner of the Caucasus or in North Persia I would be surprised but not incredulous.

Forty-one species of Meconopsis are known to botanists, and twenty to twenty-five of them are more or less known to gar-deners, at least by name. All these latter are, or have been, in cultivation.

However, there have been few introductions of wild Meconopsis seed from Asia for fifteen years or more; those brought back from Nepal by the two British Museum expeditions in 1952 and 1954, led by Mr L. H. J. Williams, are the only introductions of seed in bulk since before 1939. So it is hardly surprising that the number of species in cultivation to-day has dwindled to ten or twelve. But to the general public who enjoy flowers and grow them, the blue poppy *par excellence* is *Meconopsis betonicifolia baileyi*; and we may now try to answer our first question: How has this come about when, as we have seen, a quite different blue poppy was in cultivation at Kew over a hundred years ago?

Generally speaking, the most popular, and hence the best-known, plants are the ones anybody can grow with a minimum of trouble and expense. No matter how rare or beautiful a plant may be, unless people can grow it, it remains a museum piece. Thus up to the year 1926, although a number of Himalayan poppies, blue and not blue, were in cultivation, not one of them was an easy plant, and hence not one of them was a popular plant. Therefore the general public knew little of Meconopsis. But when in that year *M. baileyi* appeared on the stands at the Chelsea Show people, captivated by its beauty, simply could not resist it. More and more amateurs tried it, and found that they could grow it without difficulty; and it quickly became one of the most popular plants of the time.

To the experts there was nothing surprising in a blue poppy as such. What *was* astonishing was the sudden appearance of a blue poppy which any duffer could grow, after nearly eighty years' trial with thirty or forty species and so little to show for it!

The plant's history as *M. baileyi* is brief. It was first found by Captain (now Colonel) F. M. Bailey during a journey with Captain Morshead across southern Tibet, in 1913. Bailey pressed a flower in his pocket-book, and it eventually came into the hands of Sir David Prain, at that time Director of Kew and an authority on the genus Meconopsis. Prain had never seen anything like it before, and, though he had only a fragment, considered it so remarkable that without hesitation he described it as a new species, to which he gave the name *M. baileyi*. The description, like the fragment, was necessarily incomplete.

Eleven years after Bailey had found his Meconopsis, Lord Cawdor and I made a botanical exploration in some of the country through which Bailey and Morshead had been the first Europeans to travel. One of my objects was to find the plants which Bailey had casually mentioned in his diary, and particularly the Meconopsis which had been called after him. I had come to the not difficult conclusion that many of them might be worth cultivating, and further, as Bailey was not a botanist, that there might be others which he had not noticed.

We found *M. baileyi* in many places; in fact, it was by no means rare in this part of Tibet, and I was able to take back to England complete herbarium specimens and a large packet of ripe seed. The specimens were immediately identified at Kew as Prain's *M. baileyi*; they supplied all the missing parts and made a complete description possible.

But they did more than that. Now that complete specimens—and, before long, living plants—of *M. baileyi* were available, they were soon recognized as being identical, or almost identical, with a little-known species called *M. betonicifolia*. The name *M. baileyi* therefore became superfluous; *M. baileyi* equalled the longer-known *M. betonicifolia*, and it is highly inconvenient to have two different names for the same plant. However, the name *M. baileyi* persisted in the catalogues of some nurserymen, because having sold the plant under that name they did not wish to change it; to do so might be bad for trade, however good for botany. Moreover, botanists, after some consultation, agreed that the new plant did not *quite* match the old; there are slight and possibly constant differences between them. It was therefore considered that it might be convenient to retain *baileyi* as a varietal name and call the plant *M. betonicifolia baileyi*. In any case it had been found at a distance of four hundred miles from where the original species had been collected, and therefore deserved a varietal name—the more so since, unfortunately, there was no living plant of *M. betonicifolia* with which to compare the countless living plants of its new relation.

Let us now turn to the history of *M. betonicifolia* itself, that plant with the tediously long name. It was discovered in Yunnan in 1886 by the Abbé J. M. Delavay, a French Catholic priest belonging to the Missions Etrangères. Abbé Delavay found it between Talifu and Likiang—names familiar to those interested in the flora of western China, whence so many of our best hardy plants have come. He made herbarium specimens and sent them, with many other species, to the Paris Museum. In due course they came into the capable hands of the distinguished botanist A. Franchet; he did not recognize this Meconopsis and described it in 1889 as a new species, which he named *M. betonicifolia* because its basal leaves bear some resemblance to those of betony.

The position in 1926 was therefore as follows: We had (1) a blue poppy discovered in Yunnan by Delavay and named by Franchet. It had been known to botanical science for forty years, but had never been in cultivation. (Delavay sent no seed to Paris.) (2) A blue poppy found by me in the same area as Bailey's plant, and undoubtedly his *M. baileyi*. This was raised from seed and gradually found its way all over the British Isles and Europe, and to Canada, the U.S.A., and New Zealand. It was presently, though not immediately, recognized to be the

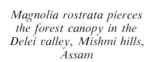

Magnolia rostrata pierces the forest canopy in the Delei valley, Mishmi hills, Assam

The milk-white dome of M. campbellii lights up the gloom of the evergreen rain forest in North Burma

Left:
*The sky-blue fragrant flowers
of Meconopsis speciosa
growing at 16,000 ft. on
barren mountain-tops in
Yunnan*

Below:
*M. betonicifolia baileyi, the
matchless blue poppy of Tibet
in the alps of North Burma*

Left:
*Meconopsis betonicifolia
baileyi in Kongbo, South-
east Tibet*

49

same as Franchet's plant,[1] though not before it had been distributed by one firm at least as *M. baileyi*. This appellation persisted, which suggests that a great many people were already cultivating it under that name (in any case less of a mouthful!). But the first name has priority; in botany *M. baileyi* has no status.

In the Royal Geographical Society's monthly record (*Geographical Journal*, Vol. 74, pp. 88–90) for July 1929, there appears the following note by the late Arthur R. Hinks, F.R.S., at that time the Society's Secretary:

At the Chelsea Show of 1926 a superb "blue poppy," *Meconopsis Baileyi*, was shown by Lady Aberconway and the Hon. H. D. Mclaren, and then first attracted general notice, though it had received an Award of Merit of the R.H.S. at their fortnightly show of the preceding April 7. In early June of the present year [1929] a large bed of the plant has flowered magnificently in Kensington Gardens, within three minutes of the Society's House, and the Director of the Royal Gardens at Kew declares that it grows like a weed—which is very unusual in the beautiful flowers which have come from the Tibetan border. . . .

Its remarkable colour, sky blue, with a touch of grey and often of lavender, and brilliant golden anthers, demands for it a place to itself, for it wrecks any usual June colour scheme. It bids fair, therefore, to become one of the most conspicuous plants in English gardens; and since in the rather unscientific, not to say commercial, atmosphere of the Chelsea Show, public attention is concentrated on the garden where it is grown in England, or on the firm which exploits the novelty, to the exclusion of any interest in the man who discovered the plant or succeeded in sending it home, we may do well to remark here that the names which should be associated with this Meconopsis are both well known in our Society. And having for greater security inquired of Major Chipp, Assistant Director of the Royal Gardens, we are able to give from his reply the following facts. In the Kew Bulletin for 1915 Sir David Prain described several new species of Meconopsis. One of them, of which he had only a fragmentary dried specimen, he named after Major F. M. Bailey, our Gold Medallist of 1916, who had collected it in the Rong Chu valley at Lunang, 10,500 feet above the sea, where it was in flower on 10 July, 1913. . . . In his paper describing the journey, and published in the [*Geographical*] *Journal* in October

---

[1] I believe that Mr W. E. Evans, of the Royal Botanic Garden, Edinburgh, was the first to perceive the likeness; or perhaps the late Dr Otto Stapf, of Kew.

1914, Major Bailey's only reference to the poppy is in the following passage (cp. 347): "Just beyond Trulung we left the Po Tsangpo and ascended the valley of the Rong Chu, up which we marched three days to Lunang, the first village which we reached in the province of Kongbo. The road was through pretty scenery, with clearings in the forest covered in flowers, among which we noticed blue poppies, purple iris, many varieties of Primula, and the poisonous aconite."

In 1924 Mr Kingdon Ward and Earl Cawdor set out to explore the remaining gap in our knowledge of the Tsangpo gorge, and found the blue poppy again in the same locality, about twenty miles north-west of the great mountain Namcha Barwa. . . . It was raised in 1925, flowered in 1926, and proved so easy to grow and so striking a success that by 1929 it had become the most famous of recent introductions. . . . The following description of *Meconopsis Baileyi* appears in Mr Kingdon Ward's book "The Riddle of the Tsangpo Gorges" (pp. 75–76):

"Beautiful as were the meadows of the *rong* . . . nevertheless, the finest flowers hid themselves modestly under the bushes, along the banks of the stream. Here among spiteful spiny thickets of Hippophäe, barberry, and rose, grew that lovely poppy, *Meconopsis Baileyi*, the woodland blue poppy. . . . Never have I seen a blue poppy which held out such high hopes of being hardy, and of easy cultivation in Britain. . . . It may be remarked in passing that the only known species of Meconopsis which bears any close resemblance to *M. Baileyi* are the Chinese *M. betonicifolia* and the Bhutanese *M. superba*."[1]

This last statement is interesting in view of the fact that Major Chipp points out that systematic botanists, including Sir David Prain, are now coming to the conclusion that the plant is probably only a geographical form of *Meconopsis betonicifolia*. It is also interesting to see how accurate has proved Mr Kingdon Ward's estimate of the adaptability of this plant to the English climate.

Thus geographers as well as botanists were interested in this plant, as they had good reason to be.

But what, it may be asked, was happening between 1884 and 1926? Why had nobody collected seed of Delavay's plant in Yunnan? For that matter, why did not Delavay himself send seed of it to Paris? He had found the plant in flower, and cannot have been insensible of its beauty. Still, Yunnan is full of

[1] Dr George Taylor, author of *An Account of the Genus Meconopsis* (1934) and the greatest living authority on the genus, tells me that this is a mistake. *M. superba* is not closely allied to *M. betonicifolia*, whereas *M. integrifolia* is.

beautiful flowers, and seventy or eighty years ago there was not that deep enthusiasm for the cultivation of hardy plants—especially in France—which has grown up and steadily increased throughout the twentieth century.

Besides, Delavay was not a botanist by profession. He was a hard-working missionary, and plant-collecting for him was merely a pleasant hobby. This spare-time occupation of his had a great influence on the future botanical exploration of Yunnan, but it came second in his life of devotion to the Missions Etrangères. He may have met with *M. betonicifolia* in the course of a day's walk from one village to another, and never thought of it again; it was just one of thousands of plants he collected—indeed, he may never have seen it again. And since he was not primarily interested in plants, he may not have noticed it in fruit, as a trained field botanist would have done. But in the light of what happened afterwards we shall not be far out if we assume that he never saw it again after he collected it in flower.

Nevertheless it does at first sight seem surprising that this plant should not have been introduced during the first decades of the present century. Between 1904 and 1932 George Forrest spent many years plant-hunting in Yunnan; he looked for, and found, many of the plants first seen by Delavay and introduced them into cultivation, together with many more which Delavay had never seen. Meconopsis was a genus to which Forrest paid particular attention, and he actually found no less than twelve species in Yunnan, though not one of them, as it turned out, did well enough in the British Isles to become a popular plant. Having almost pinpointed Delavay's locality for *M. betonicifolia*, he naturally searched for and found it. But strangely enough the seeds he sent home did not do well—the little plants perished as seedlings. Nor did he find it more than once or twice. Later the American Dr Joseph Rock collected it, but with no better result for horticulture.

One inescapable conclusion, I think, is that this particular poppy has always been rare in Yunnan. Many of the most famous introductions from western China are widespread, being found in any suitable locality over an area of hundreds, or even thousands, of square miles; but this is not one of them. The fact that George Forrest, whose well-trained Chinese collectors covered a lot of ground and missed very little, only came across the plant once or twice is sufficient endorsement for the view that *M. betonicifolia* is a very rare plant in Yunnan. Yet, even while making every allowance for the difficulties and uncertainties, it seems extraordinary that forty years elapsed between the first discovery of this Meconopsis and its introduction to Europe.

Now we come on a possible clue to the secret of its failure in Great Britain, for it seems that seeds germinated in Edinburgh, but did not live to flower. The species, as found in Yunnan, is an outpost on the outermost fringe of its distribution, and quite possibly it is dying out there—it may already have died out. This suggests a certain debility, a lack of vigour, in the plant, at least in the Yunnan form of it.

In the Tsangpo valley region, however, Bailey's poppy is not rare; though one would hardly call it common either. And at this opposite end of its distribution *M. betonicifolia* has a strong constitution. If one knew that it grew there, flowering in June and July, one could hardly fail to find it; but even if one knew that, it might prove difficult to find *out* of flower. Thus Bailey did horticulture a real service by noticing it and collecting a flower.

Twice since 1924 I have come across this lovely plant again— first, in 1926, when exploring the Seinghku valley, a tributary of the Adung, at the sources of the Irrawaddy, in northernmost Burma, and again, in 1930, on a tributary of the Lohit River, which flows into the Brahmaputra.

The Lohit River location below the Dri pass is 175 miles in an air line south-east of the Tsangpo Gorge, where the blue poppy grows in Tibet. Continuing in the same direction for another seventy-five miles over the Irrawaddy–Brahmaputra watershed, one reaches the Seinghku valley location, where it is abundant. And two hundred miles south-east of the Seinghku valley is Hoching, in Yunnan, Delavay's *locus classicus*.

Taking the Tibetan village of Lunang, where Bailey first noticed it, as centre, and a radius of twenty miles, a circle so described would probably cover all the country in that region where, in suitable places, it could be expected to grow. Thus it might occur scattered over a thousand or 1500 square miles, but not very much more. Now, if we draw a line from Lunang almost due south-east to Hoching it will pass through all the four localities where Bailey's poppy has been collected. The total distance is about 450 miles in a straight line.

However, there is no reason to think that in the other three areas this plant would be found over a thousand square miles, or anything like it; but there is good reason to think that its distribution might be continuous from Lunang to Hoching. In fact, a straight line joining Bailey's *locus classicus* to Delavay's really best shows the distribution as known to us. And all forms found north-west of Hoching are robust plants, hardy, and easy to grow in Great Britain.

It is now clear why *M. betonicifolia* and not *M. simplicifolia*, discovered forty years earlier, is *the* blue poppy; and why the former, though it has been known in botanical circles since 1889, is still regarded as a new plant in gardening circles, where it has been known only since 1926.

It may appear to some people that undue emphasis has been laid on 'blue' Himalayan poppies, as though there were none of any other colour. Actually there are species with white, yellow, deep red, scarlet, purple, dark blue, violet, and mauve flowers— which is almost the whole spectrum range. And to these must be added sky blue, the colour from which they chiefly derive their fame. After *M. simplicifolia* had flowered in 1848 other blue poppies, as well as red, yellow, and violet-flowered species, became known in gardens. Most of them were biennial, but so long as they seeded themselves—and many did—this was no particular disadvantage.

However, although several of these poppies do quite well in a humid climate, as in parts of Scotland, Wales, and Ireland, they will not grow just anywhere unless they have a great deal of attention. They are the spoilt children of the expert gardener, not for the generality of mankind and the rough-and-tumble of ordinary garden life. Keen amateurs look at them on the show stands or in botanic gardens, admire them from a distance, occasionally even try them—once. Then they give up the struggle. Life, they say, is too short for plants that are here to-day and gone to-morrow; although, to some gardeners, keeping to-morrow at bay is half the fascination of the game!

Then at last came Colonel Bailey's charmer, which quickly found its way into all hearts and gardens. What the future holds for the gardener who delights in Meconopsis, no one can say. Experience shows that most of the species occupy a very restricted area, and we now know where they are most concentrated; it follows that a few species may still remain to be discovered, in a region which is as large as it is difficult to explore.

·5·

The Inconstant Cherry

COME and see your carmine cherry in flower," a friend wrote to me.

So I went down to Sussex. I found the cherry planted against a south wall, and protected by a clump of trees from the south-westerly gales which come whistling in from the Channel to sweep across the South Downs. At that time it was about twenty years old, fifteen feet high, and every twig was alive with pale-pink flowers.

It was a pleasant surprise to see this tree growing quite happily in an English garden; but it was a surprise for more reasons than one. The dozen cherry stones which I had collected came from a single tree with bright carmine flowers. It grew on the sheltered bank of the Adung River, not far from the sources of the Irrawaddy.

One seed had germinated, and this tree, flowering for the fifth or sixth year, raised by Sir Frederick Stern, was the result. With it had come up some interesting botanical puzzles to which no good answers have yet been found; so it may be helpful to give a short account of the tree, as it grows in the mountains of South-east Asia.

Prunus puddum, as it used to be called, had long been known to botanists in India, where it has a wide distribution from Nepal to Assam, and thence to Yunnan. So long ago as 1896 Mr J. S. Gamble, an Indian Forester, recognized two varieties: (*a*) a very big tree—flowers crimson—March, and (*b*) a smaller tree—flowers pink (or white)—November.

During my travels in Sino-Himalaya I have often come across *P. puddum* (now *Prunus cerasoides*, the older name) in the mountains of Burma and Assam. In some parts of its territory it flowers a month or two before Christmas, and the flowers are pink. Elsewhere it flowers a month or two after the New Year, more rarely about the New Year, and the flowers then are always a rich carmine. This I had noticed, confirming Gamble's observation; and the flowering rhythm, with colour according to season, appears to be constant. That is to say, if *P. cerasoides* flowers before Christmas one year, that tree always flowers before Christmas, and the flowers are always pink. If it flowers after the New Year it always does so, and the flowers are carmine. Mid-December to mid-January is usually a close season for flowering in nature, though not invariably.

Only in one area have I ever seen what might almost be described as an intermediate colour, although it would be more accurate to describe the flowers as speckled. This effect is due, I think, to the petals being very pale pink, while the filaments of the anthers are deep pink, or even carmine. These trees were growing in the Mishmi hills above Dening, in the far corner of Assam—a region of tremendous rainfall; they flower in late October or early November.

Why, then, does the Sussex tree, which is still growing well, derived from the carmine cherry of North Burma, produce pink flowers? It still maintains the rhythm of the carmine cherry, flowering after the New Year, though two or three months later than in the Adung valley where it came from; but the colour is that of the autumn-flowering form.

It might help us to understand the problem if we had more information about the distribution of the two forms, especially if we could perceive some pattern in their occurrence, based on climate, soil, or other variable factor.

But no such pattern seems likely, and we appear to be left with a haphazard distribution. For the surprising fact is that the two colour-forms do not mix in nature. If the carmine form occurs in one area all trees in that area are carmine; if the standard shade is pink all trees are pink. Dark and light do not even meet, let alone overlap. But while all this is true for the wild trees, it does not appear to be always true for trees in cultivation. The Sussex specimen may not be exceptional.

Before the war it was usual in North Burma to plant cherry-trees round the outposts, to brighten the landscape in the spring. So cherry-trees were planted at Sumprabum, an outpost about a hundred miles north of Myitkyina. I saw them in full flower in January—which is unusually early, at least for the wild tree.

They were good almond-blossom pink, but not carmine. However, the only wild trees I saw in that region, some little distance from Sumprabum, it's true, were the true carmine cherry, flowering in April, close to the high mountains; and it is reasonable to suppose the planted trees came from thereabouts, and were of the carmine breed. Moreover, they flower in the New Year, which strengthens the belief that they come of dark-flowered parents.

What, then, has cultivation done to them that they have turned pale? Or do *all* trees start life with pink flowers, the colour changing gradually or suddenly to carmine in later life? But if so, surely one would find pink-flowered and carmine growing together, since there must be younger and older trees! And what of the changing rhythm, from October–November flowering and leaf-break to February–March flowering and leaf-break?

These are puzzles which can only be solved by observation and experiment. First, what is needed is more information about the trees growing in the forest—the distribution of light- and dark-flowered forms—and the climate and type of soil associated with each area.

Secondly, we must cultivate as many samples as possible, keeping strict records of their origin and of their subsequent behaviour. No easy task this, since the tree has been reported from many localities. It can hardly be a question of crossing, with dominant and recessive characters. The carmine and pale-flowered forms flower at different seasons and are widely separated in space, so they cannot hybridize; unless, of course, the carmine cherry is itself a hybrid. But if so, why do the colour-forms segregate?

My first close acquaintance with the carmine cherry was one of those unforgettable incidents of no particular significance. I had long wanted to visit the Adung valley. Once before I had glimpsed the oily green water of the river as it flowed deep and silent out of the jungle. High over it the trees almost met, forming a triumphal arch; they sloped at an angle from the vertical cliffs, and among their branches, like mistletoe, grew white-flowered rhododendron-bushes which looked like little flocks of birds in bridal plumage.

At this point, through a wide breach in the western cliff, the far smaller Seinghku River rushed eagerly over the rocks to mingle its milky waters with the Adung; and the long wisp of a cane suspension bridge spanned it just above the confluence, swaying to and fro in the wind set up by the rushing river. It would have been a nasty place to fall off. At the confluence the Adung itself, so calm and stately above, suddenly burst into a terrible rage as it met head on obstructing rocks and dropped several feet.

Then I had turned aside up the Seinghku valley, promising myself that next time I would continue up the Adung to the snow peaks. Now the chance had come.

It was early January when we reached the last village in Burma, four days' march above the Seinghku confluence. The few scattered inhabitants of the Adung were a vaguely Tibetan people who had come into the valley from the north, and had 'adopted' a few Daru—the peons of the upper Irrawaddy. Whence the Daru came, or who they are, is guesswork. They are a pygmy forest tribe of unknown origin.

Conditions were tough even for Tibetans, less because of the bitter cold (which anyway was confined chiefly to the passes) than because of the summer heat and the rain, which cause a perpetually damp atmosphere. But the climate of Tibetan Zayul across the passes is not very different.

Just above the village snow clung disconsolately to the trees, many of which were bare of leaves; and though the impression I got was of temperate forest, it was nevertheless evergreen and broad-leafed. Towards the bottom of the deep valley *Michelia doltsopa* was scattered sparsely. Its oyster-white shallow cups have a nacreous gleam, and it is a more beautiful tree than any magnolia, except perhaps the peerless *Magnolia campbellii*.

The Adung River hummed tunelessly to itself as it danced rippling over the pebbles. Since leaving the Seinghku confluence we had passed four large tributaries, and the main stream was now much reduced in volume; more and more did it look like a mountain stream. The glacier-fed sources of the Irrawaddy are at their lowest in January, when no snow melts; but before the end of the month the spring rise begins, and a ford just above the village soon became difficult.

A few weeks after our arrival I first noticed the carmine cherry across the river. It was dynamic. A change was stealing over the forest, heralded by the rosy purple glow of *Rhododendron magnificum*, which had burst into flower all along the river bank and far up the exposed slope. Everywhere the forest was spangled with leaf-buds bursting their bonds to display silver, pale gold, ruby, and emerald leaf-tips. Later, when the rains came, all the leaves would turn a sullen green, and become without form. Far up the hillsides, across the river from the village, the deep snows of winter were softening as the days lengthened and the sun came north again; and at ever shorter intervals avalanches came sliding and leaping down the deadly gullies. One by one, the enormous rocks in the river, which were high and dry when we arrived, disappeared beneath the waves. The Adung rose like a cobra poised to strike. "Stand still," it hissed, "I am death!" No longer did we dare to wade across the ford.

But on the far bank opposite our camp, almost overhanging the turbulent water, the first carmine cherry opened its flowers. It was a big tree, sturdy and tall as an oak, and leafless. But now every twig was a blaze of colour, as though red-hot lava had oozed out of little fissures in the bark and congealed.

During the next fortnight scattered cherries were coming into flower higher up. It was as though they had been switched on one by one like city lights at dusk. All of them were difficult to reach, and it was almost impossible, when the glow faded, to pinpoint them. They were lost in the vast sombre depths of the forest.

However, the first one, on the opposite bank, was easy to reach and always recognizable. It grew beside the river on the edge of a terrace which had once been under cultivation (and might be again), standing head and shoulders above its immediate neighbours. We had gazed at it from our camp a hundred times while it was in flower, and had often crossed over to get a closer view.

At this point the Adung, one of the main springs of the many-sourced Irrawaddy, is six thousand feet above sea-level, sunk deep within the mountains. Immediately above the village the ranges rise to twelve thousand feet, and a mile upstream, where the valley turns sharply, snow slopes form the middle distance, and beyond them, but hidden from view, sharp rock pinnacles rise like Gothic spires amid the huddled glaciers. In January the river had been crystal-clear, and the whole valley beyond the village of six grass-thatched huts slept beneath its dazzling quilt under the turquoise dome of heaven. But as spring came a tumult of turbid water from the melting glaciers and frequent snow-falls hurtled down the gorge, grinding the unseen boulders together like peppercorns, and to the rising roar of the waves was added a muffled and ominous rumbling. Every day larger rocks were being flung against the bamboo legs of the trestle bridge; within a few days it was battered to bits, and the wreckage swept on down the river.

Now the only way of crossing the Adung was by the cane suspension bridge, which needed a cool head and good balance. However, we continued to visit the cherry-tree, so that we could collect both flower and leaf specimens.

Later we broke camp and went north with the sun, up through the gorge to the very tip-top of Burma, where it wedges itself into the Tibet plateau. They were fantastic marches. The river filled the gorge with thunder till the echoes were flung back and forth; spray spouted up in fountains, wetting the tree-tops. We climbed through an avenue of rosy purple rhododendron mixed with maples and other broad-leafed trees. At last we reached conifer forest, then scrub, and finally grassy slopes where, later, Primulas and Meconopsis would grow—the Burmese Alps.

It was November when we returned to our camp by the village. The rains had ceased, the sky was blue; it was already cold. The fruits had long since fallen from the cherry-tree, and its leaves were turning yellow. But though we went to work with a will, scratching like flightless birds for cherry-stones, we found very few. Several inches of vegetable mould, soft, unctuous, and black, formed the carpet in which the fruits had fallen; but most of the stones were rotten, or punctured by insects, or cracked open by squirrels. The wonder is that *any* cherry-stones survive to germinate and grow into trees! The final result was about a dozen viable seeds. Perhaps that is why the carmine cherry, though not rare, is so widely scattered in the forest. But how does it get scattered? Probably by the birds which eat the cherries. Though nowhere abundant, it occurs over an immense territory.

As already recorded, under the skilful care of Sir Frederick Stern, one stone germinated. At the time of writing[1] the tree is twenty-seven years old, and has flowered for the last ten years at least.

Yet how unlike its parent in the Adung valley it is! People

[1] 1958.

have said that the initial mistake was mine—that I did not collect the carmine cherry at all, but the pink form. If that were true there would of course be no problem. But it is impossible. Only the one colour-form—the carmine cherry itself—grows in the Adung valley; never do both forms share the same locality.

I made no mistake; but from seeds of the carmine cherry one tree came up, and it was the pink form. So the colours do not breed true—at least, the carmine form evidently does not. But is it, so to speak, a reversible reaction? That is to say, could a carmine form come out of a pink cherry? Nobody knows. But what we do know is that in the *forest* the carmine and the pink each breeds true, since the colours are segregated. And that is true for the curious speckled form from the Mishmi hills also. In my experience nowhere do any of the three colour-forms overlap, or even meet. Each is isolated, confined to several discrete areas. What is the explanation?

It was in North Burma again, but not quite so far north, that I had my next close-up view of the carmine cherry in full bloom. I was collecting in the Hpimaw hills close to the China frontier, and the occasion was memorable for the multitude of brilliantly coloured birds assembled in the tree. Vivid green Chloropsis, iridescent honeysuckers, and even plain babblers, besides others I did not recognize—thirty or forty birds altogether, of probably ten or twelve species, were present. They came and went, or moved on to other branches of the tree with flutterings and cries, some of them stupid with excitement. It was a fine day at the end of March, and the breeding-season had come round again. Birds were prodding at the dangling bunches of flowers with scimitar- or awl-shaped or curved, needle-like beaks, picking up small flies and beetles, seasoning them with honey, twittering happily, and jostling in their greed. Yet there was plenty for all. Not a leaf was visible to dim the blaze; every twig was encrusted with red blossom, while a steady rain of petals and whole flowers drifted down through the outflung branches, colouring the dark earth below.

After the war my wife and I went to Manipur, which lies between Burma and Assam. Manipur had long been famous for its orchids, and particularly for the blue Vanda. It had been less explored for other plants.

Except for the vale of the Manipur River, where Imphal, the garden capital of the State, stands surrounded by moats and hills, Manipur is a highland country. Near the village of Ukhrul the highest mountain in the State, called Sirhoi Kashong, lifts its rounded head to 8445 feet; while Ukhrul itself straddles a ridge six thousand feet above the sea. These may be paltry heights for hardy plants; but the region is on the flank of Sino-Himalaya and so worthy of botanical exploration.

All around Ukhrul, in late February, the cherry-trees were flaming into flower on the wooded hillsides. They suggested a heavy rash over the dark face of the forest, for it was the true carmine cherry, *Prunus cerasoides rubea*. It was not rare, but no two trees ever grew close together; nor was it nearly as common as the snowy white pyramids of crab-apple, flowering at the same time.

The problem, as usual, was to select a tree which could be recognized and easily reached long after the flowers were over, and the bare branches clothed with leaves, when the tree had, in fact, merged into the anonymous forest. And this, of course, would be in the rainy season, when the hills are muffled in mist, and the heavy rain adds its own perplexities and discomforts.

At last we found a large spreading tree with a wealth of flowers standing close beside a path; we could follow the ripening cherries under their increasing cloak of foliage through the weeks.

After the break of the monsoon thick mists rolled over the hills, hiding everything for days on end. In July we returned from a wet tour. The gullies, so long dry, were filled with foaming water, the paths hidden in the surge of leech-infested undergrowth. However, we found our cherry-tree. The hard, sour fruits had ripened meanwhile and lay on the sodden ground; they do not hang on the tree long after they are ripe, but fall, or are knocked off by the wind and the rain. This time we picked up several hundred cherry-stones. At least half of them sank immediately in water, and could be counted on as viable.

At that time I was working for the New York Botanical Garden, so the seeds crossed the Atlantic and were distributed among a number of American subscribers. The carmine cherry would not be hardy in New York, or in any of the eastern States, both the summer heat and the winter cold being too extreme for it; but in Florida and the Gulf States, and on the Pacific coast (notably California), they should grow well.

That was ten years ago, and any trees raised from Ukhrul cherry-stones ought to be near flowering age by now, may even have flowered.[1] It would be of the greatest interest to know whether the flowers are dark or light; but I have heard no news of them from American gardeners.

Twice more in recent years I have come across the carmine cherry, on both occasions in Burma. In fact, *P. cerasoides* is distributed throughout all the mountains of Burma north of Rangoon.

In 1953 my wife and I explored part of the watershed between the eastern and western branches of the Irrawaddy north of Myitkyina, where the peaks rise to nearly twelve thousand feet. At Sumprabum, on January 5, the planted cherries were already in flower—not carmine, but a good pink, warm and satiny, like pink tulips. Later we collected seed of these trees.

Across the river in the Triangle, however, we saw only the true carmine cherry, round the little village of Arahku; and these flowered in April. Yet the trees planted at Sumprabum must be local trees, though they don't necessarily come from Arahku, which is some distance away; probably from much closer.

A story is told of the Japanese occupation of Burma. The Commander-in-Chief lived in a bungalow in Thandaung, which is a hill station in southern Burma. The bungalow belonged to a British Gurkha officer who had served many years on the frontier with the Burma Military Police; he loved the country, and, before he retired from the Army, built himself a small house in Thandaung.

In due course he retired from active service and went to live there. Shortly afterwards the war broke out, and he rejoined the Army in Burma. When the great retreat to India took place he did not expect ever to see his home again.

Nevertheless after the Japanese had been driven out of Burma and the war was over he went back to Thandaung, and great was his astonishment and joy to find his house with its neat garden intact in the midst of desolation. It was a wonderful homecoming; even the cherry-trees which he had planted himself were in flower to welcome his return.

[1] (1958). But the seeds of cherries sometimes do not germinate for one or two years after sowing.

After a time questions were asked, and it was the Japanese Commander-in-Chief himself who gave the explanation. He had seen the trees in flower round his house, and had been touched. In Japan cherry-trees are near sacred, and to desecrate them is impious. Anyone who cultivated cherry-trees must be a man and a brother; he therefore gave orders that on no account were they to be damaged. And while trees were ruthlessly cut down everywhere, the cherry-trees were spared. Before the Japanese were driven out, as many foreign houses as possible were razed to the ground; but this one, where his beloved cherry-trees were carefully tended, was not injured.

It may be remarked in passing that *P. cerasoides*, though much cultivated in Japan, is not found wild there. Formosa, however, the Liu Kiu islands, and the Chinese mainland opposite to it (Fokien), has produced a gorgeous cherry with flowers of deep carmine, which botanists call *Prunus campanulata*. Unfortunately, it is not hardy in Britain.

But anyone who wants to know what the carmine cherry is like should visit Kew Gardens in May, where in the great temperate house he may see *P. campanulata* in full bloom. The flowers, hanging in clusters, are the same open bell shape, and exactly the same deep colour as *P. cerasoides*. The leaves have the same serrate margin and acute apex. Many botanists would say they are almost exactly the same plant. Nor is *P. campanulata* the only plant with an intermittent distribution from Formosa to the Himalaya. But *P. campanulata* is carmine. So far as I know, no pink-flowered form has ever been reported.

Our latest journey to Burma in search of hardy plants was in 1956. We went to Mount Victoria in the southern Chin hills. Mount Victoria, though ten thousand feet high, is in the tropics, so not all the plants we collected there are hardy. Nevertheless some of those found on the summit appear to be true alpines, and might well prove to be good rock-garden plants.

At two villages on the mid-slopes of the mountain, cherry-trees were planted before the war; but the flowers were long over when we arrived in March, nor did they open before we left early in December.

However, when we climbed Mount Victoria in November for the last time a cherry, which outwardly looked very like *P.*

cerasoides (pink), was in full bloom in the evergreen forest at about seven thousand feet altitude. Though no two trees grew cheek by jowl, it was locally abundant. The trees were in all stages of leaf and flower, the best being quite leafless. Some, however, were fully fledged, with bronze-purple young leaves, among which the pale flowers showed wanly. There were several intermediate stages from naked trees in full bloom to leafy trees bearing pink flowers scarcely visible among the new foliage.

Later, on comparing specimens of this tree with true *P. cerasoides*, in London, I came to the conclusion that the Mount Victoria tree was not this species at all! It now looked quite different; the much smaller calyx, differently shaped, the persistent bracts and long drip-tip to the leaf, with other minor differences, suggested a different species altogether. Nor is it certain that the tree planted at Mindat—of which we obtained seed—was the same as those growing higher up on the mountain; at least their flowering seasons are different. That might, however, be due to difference of altitude.

Two thousand feet below, the planted trees had as yet shed hardly a leaf, though many had turned bright yellow. There was no sign of flowers or of new leaves. Of the Mindat cultivated trees, I collected a large quantity of seed which was sent to the United Kingdom, the U.S.A., Italy, and New Zealand.

Finally, Mr Frank Ludlow found trees of the carmine cherry a hundred feet tall, flowering magnificently, in the forests of Pome, north of the Tsangpo Gorge, in Tibet. This seems to be its farthest north.

I feel that *P. cerasoides*, whether pink, white, or carmine, must by now be in cultivation somewhere besides Sussex.

The valley of the Lohit River on the frontier between Assam and Tibet

A well-grown tree of the carmine cherry as it grows in the mountains of North Burma and Assam

·6·

Some Primulas

PRIMULA is a hallowed name, and there can be few gardens in this country where not one is grown. Botanists have described about six hundred species, and much has been written about the many which are in cultivation. Their habit, or manner of growth, their habitat and surroundings, their relationships to one another, their distribution in space, and above all the best way to grow them—all these matters, and more, have been studied and recorded many times. But very little has been written about their actual appearance in nature and their frequency on the ground.

> A primrose by a river's brim
> A yellow primrose was to him,
> And it was nothing more.

Whether the effect on "him" of a hundred, or a thousand, primroses by the river's brim was simply a matter of mathematical calculation I am not prepared to say. But I have to tell of primulas in thousands and tens of thousands, and can say positively that astronomical numbers of primulas, when they are sufficiently concentrated to leave their mark on the landscape, arouse emotions different not only in degree but in kind from those aroused by a solitary plant, however strange or beautiful or unexpected it may be.

To the geographical botanist the most interesting plants of any large genus are the outliers. These are the species which, having travelled farthest from their centre of origin and reached the frontiers, have got cut off. If they succumb we are of course unlikely to hear about it. But if they survive, their distribution is then discontinuous, and in course of time they may—and often do—change their appearance so much that they are no longer the same species. They have ventured too far afield, and in their new world have themselves become new. They have reached the point of no return. So far as is known, all plants —even plants of the same species—seek *Lebensraum*. Some are more successful than others, which adds to the diversity and beauty of the world, and of course to its interest. Only uniformity is dull.

I propose to tell of some primulas in the field. What I have to say has no direct bearing whatever on how to cultivate them in the garden. It may, however, be regarded as a tailpiece to what has already been written about them.

But first, speaking of outliers, we must note that of the grand army of primulas which has marched triumphantly across Eurasia from the Atlantic to the Pacific, and less flamboyantly through North America, only two or three species have dared to cross the equator, and have lived to tell the tale. One of them found a congenial home on the top of a volcano in Java, and stayed there to earn a name for itself—*Primula imperialis*. Though it is no longer in touch with the mainland, it is almost identical with the East Indian *Primula prolifera*, itself an outlier confined to the Khasi hills of Assam. The distance between the two localities is about 2500 miles.

So alike are these two that one name (*Primula prolifera*) was originally enough for both. Then, with more precise discrimination, the Java plant was raised to specific rank and became *P. imperialis*. When this happens to two plants separated by a wide gap one is apt to suspect (though the suspicion is perhaps an unworthy one) that botanists, unable to account for such a broken distribution, cut the Gordian knot by making one species into two. Not that that helps. Rather does it make the task of the geographer more difficult. The difference between the two plants is not thereby increased, and he is put to the trouble of discovering for himself that the two are practically the same. He still has to account for their disjunction.

Here the gap can be reasonably explained away by assuming that at some previous time the distribution of *P. prolifera* was continuous from Assam to Java; and therefore that the land too was continuous. In other words, Java formed part of the mainland. One must also invoke the aid of the Sino-Himalayan ice-age, which, by altering the climate throughout South-east Asia, caused such a flutter in the settled vegetation that almost all plants got pushed around. But eventually they settled again, though into new patterns.

As to the continuous land theory, the sea around the Malay peninsula as far east as Borneo and as far south as Java is so shallow that there is no difficulty at all in believing that it was once dry land, and that at no very distant epoch. This conclusion is strongly supported by the distribution of mammals and birds in the archipelago. Further, there is ample evidence that the glaciers of Sino-Himalaya were larger, more numerous, and extended much farther south than they do to-day; factors making for continual changes of climate throughout, as the ice waxed and waned.

More surprising than the chance stranding of *P. imperialis* on a Javanese volcano is the chance isolation of the mysterious *Primula magellanica* in the Strait of Magellan. This plant has been cut off many thousands of miles south of the nearest primula of any other sort or kind, and completely severed from its own special group; for *P. magellanica* is *Primula farinosa* in fancy dress, with distance in space and time to lend what enchantment it may.

If you were to pay a visit to Tierra del Fuego, below the 50th parallel south of the equator, you might, or might not, come across *P. magellanica*; but more likely 'not' than 'might.' It has been found only once, though searched for many times since. However, north of Magellan there is *Primula decipiens*, and still farther north, *Primula comberi*; and they all belong to the Farinosa clan—are, indeed, blood relations. After that, continuing northward, you will not meet with a primula, Farinosae or otherwise, for over five thousand miles. At least, if you do you will make botanical history.

We can only suppose that the bridge by which *P. magellanica* and its friends crossed the equator was the continental divide. This great mountain system is continuous from Vancouver to Cape Horn, and forms the watershed between the Atlantic and the Pacific. It may well have been along this highway that the plants, retreating south during the ice-ages, marched. There is, moreover, an element of timing here too; for no primula could have crossed from North America to South America *before* the isthmus of Panama was uplifted. Five hundred miles of ocean lay between the continents.

Not even the most enthusiastic rock gardener would go to

the Andes in search of primulas to-day, since he knows it is
virtually certain he would not find any.

What, then, has happened to them—if they ever existed? Why
did nature scrap them? And how comes it that *P. magellanica*
and one or two stout allies were dropped at the end of the journey
and forgotten, and *survived*? This is a matter for speculation.

However, it seems certain that some species of primula, if only
the immediate ancestors of *P. magellanica* and *P. decipiens*—so
very like *P. farinosa* itself—at some time grew along the entire
length of the Andine ranges, just as they do to-day along the
entire length of the Rockies and the Sierra; and as *Primula
denticulata*, for example, does along the Himalaya from Kashmir
to Yunnan.

Plants, least of all primulas, do not leap the length and breadth
of continents in a few great kangaroo hops. They move on
sedately, stage by stage, through millennia, so long as conditions
suit them. But when conditions change the distribution of species
also changes. This is what appears to have happened in the
Andes, where great changes of climate have taken place, especially since the ice-age, tearing gaps thousands of miles wide in
species continuity, as the links in the primula chain broke. Similar
gaps in species continuity occur in the Himalaya. But here, because the mountain ranges trend east and west rather than north
and south, the gaps are far shorter.

I might add that it is only since the disappearance of primula
for nearly six thousand miles south of California that the distribution of *P. magellanica* and its nearest neighbours becomes remarkable. There is nothing particularly curious in its occurrence
so far south as Magellan, any more than there is anything curious
in the occurrence of *P. farinosa* in the sub-arctic. What *is* remarkable is that the Andes should be so bereft of primulas in general,
and of *P. farinosa* in particular. The genus stops abruptly in
North America in about latitude thirty-five degrees north
(*Primula incana*); it begins again with *P. comberi* in about latitude forty degrees south.

As an appendix to the story of the one which was left behind
and forgotten in South America I will add a strange story from
Burma.

P. farinosa itself is a small north-temperate plant with mealy
leaves and mauve flowers with a yellow 'eye.' Variously

accoutred, it occurs right across the Eurasian continent from the Atlantic to the Pacific, and all round the Polar Sea—the most widespread of all primulas. Yet, so it was believed, it had never reached the Himalayas, nor even crossed the great Asiatic divide.

However, one day in June 1942 my path lay over the Diphuk La in the extreme north of Burma, on a long walk to India. The pass, about 14,500 feet, was at that late date almost clear of snow, at least on the Burma side; and the meadow on the Tibetan side, a thousand feet down, was spongy with water—almost a swamp. We splashed through the soft sphagnum moss, expecting every moment to go in knee-deep. Here among the moss and grass I was surprised to find the surface spangled with colonies of a primula so minute that it appeared at first sight to be floating like duckweed. It had mauve flowers, and was in fact none other than one of the many Protean forms of *P. farinosa*. I collected specimens, but regrettably, in the course of a somewhat confused journey, all but one or two were lost. However, enough were saved for the purposes of identification, and *P. farinosa* (or a very close relative) it proved to be. It was the last place in the world one would have expected to find a plant which grows in Yorkshire; but Burma's icy mountains no doubt hide other dark secrets!

There is a second example of discontinuous distribution among primulas in Assam. It is less dramatic than that of *P. prolifera*, since it involves a gap of only 275 miles, and no obviously broken bridge; but more personal, since I observed it myself.

Primula sherriffiae had been discovered in the foothills of Bhutan by Major George Sherriff twenty years previously. When I saw it for the first time growing wild I was so overcome by its exquisite beauty that I could say nothing. It was rapture just to sit and look at it.

Though it proved tender, as one would expect, it had been successfully grown under glass and was quite happy in the alpine house. Its discovery in the Manipur hills was interesting, not because the two localities are far apart—they aren't—but because they are sundered by the whole width of the low, hot Brahmaputra valley or plain of Assam, a hundred miles across. A primula can no more leap such a barrier than it can leap the fifty miles of sea between Malaya and Sumatra.

This is briefly the story of how we found *P. sherriffiae* in Manipur, whither we had gone on a different quest.

May had been an unusually wet month. Now it was June, and the weather shortly before the monsoon broke was delicious. This was the very time to be on the hilltops, not down in Ukhrul, a mere six thousand feet above sea level. Our principal objective was the summit of Sirhoi Kashong, 8445 feet, about twelve miles from Ukhrul; nor could we have chosen a better day than June 5 for the long walk.

At crack of dawn we were on our way, walking fast. Before noon we were high up on the mountain among the lilies we had come so far to see. But a more unexpected thrill was in store. We had just finished our picnic lunch, and were about to move on to the summit, only a few hundred yards distant. At that moment my wife happened to glance up the slope at a rock which cropped out near the crest of the ridge. I noticed her gaze suddenly riveted, and I glanced in the same direction—and stared, transfixed. What *could* I be looking at? A rock plant certainly, because it grew on the side of an otherwise bare rock, and was—well, what colour was it? One of those anonymous pastel colours which can only be vaguely described by comparison with something better known, like bonfire-smoke, or the blue of distant hills before rain.

We scrambled up the grassy slope and sat there before it, entranced. The warmth had brought out the sweet fragrance strongly; it hung over us like a rosy cloud. I knew instinctively what it was, because I had once, years before, seen a black-and-white picture of it; but never would I have expected to find such a plant here. Primulas of that kind were, in my experience, high alpines, sleeping half their lives under a quilt of snow. For minutes we sat spellbound, silent and filled with awe, so beautiful was *Primula sherriffiae*, and so totally unexpected.

We hunted assiduously all over the summit for more plants, searching every rock outcrop, every stony bank, likely or unlikely, with fair success, though *P. sherriffiae* was not a common plant here. Nor in such a limited area (since it did not descend below eight thousand feet) could we expect it to be abundant.

On a later occasion, climbing down a steep gulch which furrowed the south slope, we turned a sharp corner and came face to face with a cliff so thickly plastered with primula that the plants appeared to be growing on top of one another; and every one was in full bloom. Each scape bore three, four, or rarely five flowers, till there were hundreds of them almost touching each other. They looked like a large bunch of flowers clenched in a giant's fist, and through the shifting mist they waxed and waned like Bengal lights.

To explain how *P. sheriffiae* came to grow in two such exclusive spots, nearly three hundred miles apart, we must suppose either that the climate of the valley was formerly very different, or else that the plant did not migrate directly across it. If we accept the latter view we must find an alternative route to link up the two localities. Luckily one is close at hand: the conclusion is that the primula followed a much longer route round the head of the Assam valley, keeping to the hills the whole way. Nor is that the least likely explanation. The ranges flanking the Assam valley converge gently towards the apex of the plain, to meet finally where three great rivers rush out of the mountains and unite to form the Brahmaputra.

Again, it should be pointed out that there is nothing remarkable about the occurrence of *P. sherriffiae* in Bhutan and in Manipur; nor for that matter about the presence of *P. prolifera* in Assam, and its almost looking-glass likeness, *P. imperialis*, in Java. It is the *gaps* in the chain which are remarkable—missing links which have to be accounted for.

None of the primulas mentioned so far can be called popular garden plants, though they serve admirably to illustrate the botanical interest which is part of the joy of plant-hunting. I will therefore describe the finding of two well-known species, both of which have been in cultivation for over thirty years.

The most frequent adverse criticism of *Primula florindae* is that it is rather coarse, by which the critic invariably means large. Certainly it *is* large, much larger than most species met with in gardens. But no one who had seen it growing by the great river of Tibet would have thought it large by Tibetan standards. It is a matter of scale, and of proportion. Grown in a small mound built of small, haphazard bits of rock, among which small plants are perched like flies on a stale bun, *P. florindae* can look as coarse as Gulliver looked among the Lilliputians; a triton among minnows.

Its basal sheaf of long-stalked heart-shaped leaves, its broomstick stem, rising to three feet or more, dusted with flour-like meal and crowned by an immense mop of yellow Burmese-bell-shaped flowers, needs a bold background. A single plant is big and bold enough to stand alone if the surroundings are big and bold. But *P. florindae* is one of those plants which looks its best growing in a crowd, as nature intended it to grow, challenging the current. It is the forest of stems rising above the curved leaves, like frail masts from a rough green sea, which is the attraction; not the lone specimen. A stream, blocked by colonies of *P. florindae* in flower, is for ever a bit of the Tibetan plateau. The size of the large basal leaves ensures room for the flower scapes to display themselves; but the flowers themselves are so crowded that while they shake themselves free from the mop you get the feeling the remainder must explode like a rocket, and send a cloud of scented yellow stars drifting to earth.

My first sight of it was undramatic. We had crossed the Temo La, a pass about fourteen thousand feet high, and after a long descent had come at last to the forest which filled the valley. But as we continued to descend, forest in fact no longer quite filled it; where the stream ran, the ground was marshy, and meadow replaced the dark fir-trees.

It was early June, but snow still lay in wads and patches in the forest. However, the grass was coming up, leaf-buds were opening, and had already thrown a thin green mantle over the broad-leafed trees, and galaxies of flowers eagerly greeted the carnival of summer. Near the village where we intended to stay we reached a stream overshadowed by trees. Here in the half-shade large clumps of primula clogged the bed, holding up the flow of water. Already the scapes were visible among the crowded leaves. The water gurgled among stones, and there was mud underneath. I thought, soon they would block the stream entirely, so tightly were they packed, like flag irises in a ditch at home. At first I could discern only a single species, but some days later, as the leaves reached their full size, two kinds clearly separated themselves out of the crowd and proclaimed their independence.

Day after day I visited the colony, noting that the two species (I wondered now how I could ever have confused them!) hardly mingled except at the edges. One was confined to running water in the stream-bed itself; the other grew near the bank and thence invaded the marshy meadow above, where it occupied every foot of open ground. The flowers of both, but not the leaves, recalled the well-known *Primula sikkimensis*.

The larger plant of the two (*P. florindae*) had enormous heart-shaped leaves, broad at the base and round at the top, dark-green, with jagged margins, carried on tall, upstanding stalks. They looked like shields. By the time this primula colony had come of age, about the end of June, the white masts were three feet high, and the hundreds of flowers scented the air.

Meanwhile the lesser plant with long narrow-oval or oblong leaves, which have an unusual finely and evenly puckered surface, had also grown up. The flowers are an even softer yellow than those of the other, owing to a broad band of white meal just inside the bell-shaped corolla, and are borne in tiers, or whorls. The stem, after unfurling one cluster of flowers, continues to lengthen, growing right through them, then unfurls a second cluster above the first. And this may happen a third time, so that several flower-clusters seem to be impaled at equal intervals on the wand-like stem.

Half a mile down the valley, where the stream spilled over into the meadows, this species (*Primula alpicola luna*) grew in dense crowds, which in full bloom made an unforgettable picture. There were thousands of closely packed plants, with tens of thousands of pale moonlight-yellow bells swinging in the breeze. I named it the moonlight primula, because its radiant flowers seemed to reflect some invisible source of light.

This fertile pasture, locally called the *rong* (the Tibetan name for a grazing valley) was flanked on either side by a high and bulky mountain range, which reached above the timber line. Looking downstream one could see, on clear days, over the tops of the trees, a cluster of snowy peaks not far away. Eastward, and separated from us by one of these rocky ranges, the great river of Tibet skidded and jerked as it edged round the snow pinnacle of Namcha Barwa, the twenty-five-thousand-foot steeple crowning the Assam Himalaya; then battered its way into a forested gorge ten thousand feet deep. Everything was on a majestic scale, and so small a thing as a primula had to be not only big of its kind, but massed in countless numbers, to make so much as a ripple on the enormous surface of the landscape.

But this both *P. florindae* and *P. alpicola* contrived to do. Nature, too often thrifty of its charms, is sometimes generous. In the *rong* the meads above the bush-lined stream were so thickly

overgrown with the moonlight primula that no room remained
for any other plant; though where the primula grew more
sparsely, crimson Pedicularis, violet iris, and other flowers grew
in abundance. The broad sweeps of saffron shone with a pearly
lustre against the emerald-green grass. The foreground of forest
and meadow was dark against the flanking ranges, which in turn
led on ridge by ridge beyond the large outposts of the forest to
the blue arc of heaven overhead, where snow peaks stood sentinel
on the edge of the world.

We ascended two thousand feet out of the *rong,* up through
the diminishing forest, to the barren windswept crest of the ridge;
and suddenly the view opened out. Eastward, range beyond
range, the skeleton of a plateau from which the flesh had been
gnawed by glaciers and carried away by running water through
a network of scarcely visible gorges appeared; white snow peaks
and black rock towers; notches which might be passes over which
men from time immemorial had toiled from one valley to the
next; screes, which gave a clue to the rate of demolition in this
built-up region, and emphasized the lack of transport to carry off
the debris.

By the trickling streams, derived from melting snow along the
ridge, sheltering among the angular stones, primulas nestled in
small clumps, or singly. Their flowers were violet, maroon,
yellow, or rarely milk-white, set in whorls up the eighteen-inch
stems like those of *P. alpicola* in the *rong* two thousand feet
below; but generally there were more whorls—three or four
instead of one or two. So broad was the dado of meal round
the inside of the corolla that the colours, especially the deep-
violet, were diluted. All were deliciously fragrant.

There was no significant difference, except in colour and a
certain sumptuousness, between these alpine primulas and those
in the *rong—P. alpicola luna.* The violet-flowered one later received the additional name of *violacea,* and became, therefore,
P. alpicola violacea. The colour seems to be fast and breeds true.
It was rather curious that for once the high-level plants were
generally bigger than the valley form; it is more usual for the
alpine form to be the smaller. Curious too that one colour variety
should be confined to the valley, while all variations on the
theme should grow 1500 or two thousand feet higher.
But, as a matter of fact, nothing is known about the distribution
of the colour varieties which have been distinguished by name,

luna and *violacea*. The latter seems to include several colour forms, the best of which is a clear violet. The limits of these two primulas—*P. florindae* and *P. alpicola*—first found growing in company, are not well known; but it is clear that their territory in the Tsangpo valley and its tributaries is restricted. *P. alpicola luna* grows also in the country to the south between the Tsangpo and the Himalayas, where the Subansiri rises.

Eleven years passed and I returned to the valley of the Tsangpo after crossing the Himalayas farther east. But first I spent some time at the sources of the Subansiri, and it was here I saw the greatest multitude of primulas I have ever seen or imagined. Indeed, I would not have believed such a concentration possible had I not brushed through it for an hour or two.

It was the end of June, and I had reached the district of Tsari, the sacred mountain, spending several days in a small timber house near the junction of two valleys. It was the only house for miles and stood next to a monastery, also of timber, where two or three monks lived. Here the alpine region was giving place to forest, the transition marked by an extensive development of meadow, with scattered trees.

Almost the only meadow-plant visible was a yellow-flowered primula which I satisfied myself was a robust three-whorled form of *P. alpicola*. So thickly did they grow on the ground that the plants were touching one another, their leaves mingled. That other plants would grow well in the meadow, given the chance, was obvious—a blue iris for one, and that too was in flower. But it had no hope against the overwhelming advance of the primula tide.

On July 6 we continued our march down the main valley. There was no clear path. We just pushed our way through the meadow near the bubbling stream, knee-deep in the close ranks of primula, trampling them underfoot at every step. It was sacrilege, but with every yard we advanced they seemed to draw closer together, to grow more thickly, and to avoid them was impossible.

Not until we were a mile or more down the valley and well into the forest did the pressure of primulas begin to relax. By this time the meadow brook, swollen by many small tributaries, had changed its tune. We had reached the brink of an escarpment, the rough edges of which were softened by forest, but not enough to disguise the fact that it *was* an escarpment. Gone now was the soft walking through damp meadow; the winding sea of primulas lay behind us. We prepared for an uncomfortably steep descent over the rocks, our ears filled with the crash of the torrent as it plunged madly into the gorge, flinging up fountains of spray.

As the altitude rapidly decreased, so did the primulas, until soon there were none left. I cast my mind back. The morning's walk through the press of stately primulas which grew in countless millions, while we pushed our way between the tall white stems, trampling them underfoot, had been an unforgettable experience. No doubt I was bewitched by mere numbers; but not that only. Our progress stirred up clouds of fragrance which rose in an almost visible mist, and my eyes ached with the unrelieved sheets of yellow flowers, all alike. I grew giddy with the feast of scent and colour. It was something I had never experienced before, and am not likely to see again. I have, of course, seen large colonies of plants before and since—bluebells in an English oak wood, anemones in a Swedish beech wood—but these are on a far more modest scale. It is the airy spaciousness of the Tibetan scene—like the spaciousness of the sky and of the ocean—which makes the orgy of flowers unforgettable.

Of course, the dominance of *P. alpicola* implied the suppression of all other plants which otherwise would have shared the meadow; but irises, buttercups, campanulas, Pedicularis, grasses, even the all-conquering Compositae, were for once routed. All competition had been stifled at birth. The primulas had ruthlessly seized every square inch of ground, and refused to share it.

After seeing *P. alpicola* in Tibet, cultivated primulas in an English garden, on however generous a scale, inevitably look to me like samples.

·7·

Rhododendrons Unseen

ONE of the most satisfactory and enjoyable diversions I have engaged in was collecting seeds 'blind'; that is to say, collecting seeds of plants I had not seen in flower.

The great majority of alpine plants, at least, are cultivated for the beauty of their flowers; and as summer in the alps is brief, one cannot hope to see all of them in flower in a single season—one sees no more than a sample in any limited area. Though it is taking a chance to collect seeds blind, it is one fraught with exciting possibilities and well worth taking.

Thus I often hoped to find something really wonderful, something I had missed in flower, more alluring than any plant I had found hitherto; though why I should expect to notice out of flower anything I had failed to notice in flower, I cannot imagine. Still, it was just possible I might do so.

The success or failure of collecting 'blind' turns on knowing what sort of plants are worth collecting, and what they look like in winter garb, when they have died down and are perhaps half buried under snow; and further, in knowing *where* to look. A clump of dwarf Campanula or Anemone, when in flower, may be visible at some little distance; but it is almost invisible when it dies down to the ground, and can hardly be seen until one treads on it. Where, then, can one most usefully tread? There is also a large element of luck in finding in fruit or seed any plant to which one has not earlier been lured by bright colour or by scent, as butterflies are lured. But not entirely that either, for though one is collecting blind, there is no necessity to be short-sighted too! Clues exist to put you on the right track; there are trails to be followed up. Indeed, the imaginative collector can often give a more lively account of the dead than a description of the living!

One expects alpine gentians to be blue, saxifrages yellow,

asters mauve. One suspects a Meconopsis of being good rather than easy to grow, one is convinced that all primulas and rhododendrons are worth cultivating, and that every iris will be *somebody's* darling. No one would hesitate for a moment to collect any of these in fruit.

As for rhododendrons, which for fifty years have been what one might call a vogue plant, once you have put one in its correct series you have a useful clue to its colour and shape, though of course you may guess wrong. Flower colour is sometimes a very important quality, and particularly so in rhododendrons; but not all-important. If a flower-bud is opened carefully in the winter by prising off the scales one by one the flowers, perfect in miniature, will be seen carefully crumpled, each in its bud scale axil; and if they have a streak or mottle of crimson in them you may be sure the flowers will be crimson or blood-red when fully open. If no red is visible they will not. You then have a wide choice of possibilities.

Just as summer has its flowers, so has winter its fruits; and shrubs covered with berries, particularly red berries, are of course desirable for that alone, quite apart from any merit their flowers may possess. They are berried treasure, and in these days, when June-flowering shrubs are two a penny, invaluable. The same applies to autumn colour in deciduous trees, and in another context to evergreen-trees.

Since shrubs like Berberis, Cotoneaster, Viburnum, Lonicera, and Sorbus abound in Sino-Himalaya, one is certain to find some worth-while plants on a winter journey; late autumn and winter are the proper time to travel in search of autumn colour. One is not collecting blind—far from it. Coloured berries and coloured leaves are as easily noticed in winter as coloured flowers are in spring.

In those far-off spacious days when one could travel freely in the mountains of Burma and Assam, not to mention Yunnan and Tibet, I used to meditate on the advantages of an all-winter plant-hunt, travelling continuously—on foot—for several months, camping where I liked for as long as I liked, finally returning to England for the summer. I never put this plan into operation; partly, perhaps, because I was not entirely confident that I would always recognize good plants a little way off the path, and partly because I never could resist the startling joy of seeing mountains in flower in the spring. By the time I felt I could safely risk the odds it was already too late—political conditions rendered it impossible.

Several times when plant-hunting beyond the Himalayas I started back in November, and had to make long journeys over the passes in order to reach the plains; and in the course of these journeys I collected blind many of the plants mentioned above, as well as others, though with what success it is still early to say.

Once only did I deliberately set out on a long winter journey, after spending seven or eight months—spring, summer, and autumn—plant-hunting (which here means flower-hunting). On this occasion we travelled for two months, going far out of our way, spurred on not only by botanical discovery but by geographical exploration also. And this I know, that of many rhododendrons then collected 'blind,' all were good, and most were first-class. Hence a short account of this winter journey of exploration and intensive search for rhododendrons, through the gorges of the Tsangpo, may be of interest as illustrating my argument.

The cliffs of the Tsangpo Gorge tower up on either side till they seem to brush the sky, and are thickly forested below with rhododendron species growing in dense colonies amongst far bigger trees. Higher yet, in the alpine region, dwarf rhododendrons plaster the screes and rocks. In the early spring Lord Cawdor and I, after crossing the Himalaya, had followed the winding course of the Tsangpo eastward across the dry plateau of Tibet for over two hundred miles before we remarked any permanent change in the scenery and vegetation. During this time the valley had narrowed from nearly three miles in width to less than one mile; then the river began to widen again, but only the river, not the valley itself, while for many weary miles treeless sand-dunes and pebble-banks succeeded one another with monotonous regularity, the current always rather swift, even when the water-level was low. At this point we left the Tsangpo and spent the next six or seven months exploring and collecting both to the north and south of it. It was mid-November when we returned to the river. We were anxious if possible to complete Colonel Bailey's exploration of the gorges, which he had been forced to leave unfinished—and for this, in Tibet, the best season is the winter months, when the water is at its lowest. Accordingly, we continued down the Tsangpo.

Almost immediately the climate began to change, and the

vegetation changed with it. Forest began three or four days' march above the mouth of the gorge; it crept lower and lower down the mountain-sides till, as we entered the gorge proper, it reached the river itself.

Higher up there had been stretches where it was possible to cross the river in skin coracles, and even to travel downstream for several miles; but that was far back, before we reached the hairpin bend where only a high blade of rock separated us from India. In the gorge itself the river, though much narrower, was far too swift and rough even for coracles.

We halted for a few nights at a last village just within the jaws of the gorge. We could still make our way down into the river-bed, where the rocks looked as if they were simmering like red-hot lava; this on closer examination turned out to be due to layers of *Cotoneaster conspicuus* covered with thousands of scarlet berries. Loads now had to be cut down in weight, as the cliff climbing in the gorge was going to be difficult. Progress would certainly be slow, and might be reduced to a very few miles a day, so it was impossible to say exactly how much food must be carried; but we allowed a fairly wide margin.

Gyala, the last village, was at an altitude of about nine thousand feet, and after four days we expected to reach a little wooden monastery in the forest. Beyond that point our guides knew nothing—or professed to know nothing—except that the country was very difficult and nobody ever went there.

Next morning we started. From the terrace on which Gyala stands the path at once began to climb the mountain, winding steeply up through the forest, as though to get as far above the river as possible. Presently the slope eased a little. We crossed a torrent rushing down a deep gully, and then we were really inside the gorge. The path was quite well-marked, except when we had to cross a stream, when the continuation on the farther side was not always opposite the spot where it broke off on this. There were tree rhododendrons hereabouts, but they looked to be familiar species, although as they were not in flower it was impossible to be certain. But I intended to collect seed of every species I could reach.

The first night we camped on steep ground at the foot of a tall tree. It was not possible to pitch the little bivouac tent, but we rigged it up as a roof, though rain seemed unlikely. Not far up the slope a sulphur spring bubbled from the mountain-side, and next

The giant Tibetan cowslip (Primula florindae) in cultivation in Britain

By courtesy of the Royal Horticultural Society

Primula atro-crocea nodding its orange bells in the Adung valley, North Burma

P. strumosa and P. gambleiana struggle for supremacy in the Assam Himalaya, at 12,000 ft. in the region of silver fir

morning, while the men were packing the loads, we went up to examine it. There wasn't much to see, for the ground was marshy and there was thick bamboo undergrowth. Breaking through this on my way back to camp, I noticed a tangle of rhododendron, the stems rising no more than a foot above the ground; it was a low, flopping shrub with small thick leaves, and I was sure I had never seen it before.

A brief search revealed some capsules, and these looked something like the capsules of *Rhododendron boothii*; there were flower-buds too, the bud scales finely silver-fringed with hairs like spun glass. After an intensive search I secured about two dozen capsules. Little dreaming I had found what was to become a popular hardy rock-garden shrub, *R. leucaspis*, I rejoined the party and we continued our journey through the gorge. Perhaps I was lucky to have found the plant, for I did not see it again; nor is it by any count a common species.

The path continued high up on the face of the cliff, through forest which grew thicker every mile; the dampness continued to increase, favouring the growth of rhododendrons. Many unfamiliar broad-leafed trees formed the bulk of the high forest, but I found it impossible to collect everything, and concentrated on rhododendrons, which seemed to be in endless variety. Hereabouts I found a colour form of the curious *R. keysii*— I recognized it by its leaves—which normally bears bunches of little tubular flowers, red with a yellow five-toothed rim; in the Tsangpo Gorge the flowers are pure red without any yellow rim; so when it flowered in Britain it was named var. *unicolor* to distinguish it.

One smallish tree species of which I got seed looked rather like *R. arboreum*, though I did not think it was that. When it flowered in England some twenty years afterwards it proved to have rather charming furry buds and reddish-purple flowers in fat trusses, and attracted much admiration. In spring the forest would be lit up with it. Its name is *R. silvaticum*.

Next morning we awoke to find the whole forest lacquered with a film of fresh snow. Climbing up and down the slippery track, sometimes balancing on a ledge, sometimes scrambling up a ladder or over boulders, was discomforting and dangerous, and we made slow progress. The rhododendrons continued to increase in numbers and variety; the cliffs, when they were not smooth and vertical, were completely hidden by them. Some were familiar to me, others were not, to judge by outward appearances. Collecting seed in the cold, wet forest and on the icy cliffs was always unpleasant, often difficult, occasionally quite impossible.

At one point we went down from the usually high-level track right into the bowels of the gorge, alongside the thundering river; here there was a small sandy bay, now dry, with an enormous smooth rock standing almost clear by itself, gouged out of the bank by the rushing water. It was the sort of place where I would have expected to find an unusual rhododendron—and there it was, growing against the isolated boulder, a large, bushy shrub with small, very grey leaves which looked as though they had a film of electro-plating upon them. Luckily there was no need to climb the rock, which would have been difficult and time-consuming, to get it. At first sight I took it to be the plant we used to call *Rhododendron aureum* (now called *Rhododendron xanthostephanum*), a tidy grey-leafed shrub with buttercup-yellow flowers, not hardy enough in England to be popular. I had often seen *R. xanthostephanum* in flower, and knew it pretty well by sight; on closer examination this Tsangpo shrub did not altogether look the part, yet I would have been hard put to it to say from memory exactly how it differed. I was convinced, however, that had the two plants been growing here side by side I should never have confused them. The new plant just looked slightly different—perhaps greyer, or it had a trimmer habit and smaller leaves; it might indeed have passed for a variety of the other.

On the other hand, I should have been at least mildly surprised to find *R. xanthostephanum* itself here. This was by no means the type of forest in which I had seen it growing in North Burma.

Not all these comparisons passed through my mind at the moment of seeing this rhododendron; some of them came when I was examining the specimens I had pressed, later. My business in such an unexplored place was to collect seed of every rhododendron I could find; and even if I had been virtually certain that this was my old friend I should have collected seed of it first and argued about it afterwards.

For above all I had to be quick. All this stopping and collecting took time, and the porters, in spite of their loads, got along faster than I did. Already they were some distance ahead; and as there were difficult spots where I might need help, or moral support, I did not want to be left too far behind. Nor was it always clear where the path lay.

So I went over the bush as fast as I could, picking off the little capsules and stuffing them into my bag till I had gathered every one I could reach. None of them had opened, which was fortunate; but clearly they were ripe, and were only waiting for a spell of dry weather to split, and scatter their gold-brown seeds, most of which would be washed away by the river when it rose in the spring.

When I saw this plant again some years later, growing in an English garden, it was as large as the shrub from which I had collected seed. It was not *R. xanthostephanum*. The flowers were not so bright a yellow, the foliage a little greyer, duller; on the other hand, it had the advantage of growing better and of being much hardier. It was named *Rhododendron auritum*.

I never came across it again in Tibet, and perhaps I was lucky ever to have found it. I had really scrambled down to the very bottom of the gorge because it offered one of the rare opportunities to get an altitude reading of the river; the track ran a little above the sandy cove.

That *R. auritum* is not a common plant is suggested by the fact that when some time later the well-known plant explorers Mr F. Ludlow and Major Sherriff spent two years exploring this corner of Tibet, accompanied at various times by Mrs Sherriff, Dr George Taylor (now Director of the Royal Botanic Gardens, Kew), and others, they only once came across it. So my *alter ego* must have led me to it.

On the fourth day we reached a wide bay in the iron flank of the great mountains. In front of us rose the snow-covered ridge of Sanglung, leading upward to a peak almost as high as Namcha Barwa itself; and in a hollowed terrace from which some of the forest had been cleared stood a small timber house. This was the monastery of Pemakochung, the abode of two missionary monks who were absent, probably away over the mountains converting to Buddhism the heathen tribesmen in the south. All round us, as in a fairy-tale, was the forest. We decided to rest here a day—or rather, to let the porters rest—while we tried to ascend one of the spurs and reach the alpine meadows.

In the morning we started. But the tangled rhododendron undergrowth was so thick that we had to hack our way through, and it was soon certain we could not reach the meadows and get back the same day. The going was too rough, and anyhow the meadows were under deep snow. However, we reached a spur, or was it an ancient moraine?—and struggled up through dense rhododendron scrub, composed almost entirely of one species with remarkable leaves: large, broadly oval in shape, very bristly, and as hard as a board. The shoots were shaggy, with several years' persistent bud scales hanging to them, shrivelled, but defiant and very untidy.

When many years later it flowered in England nobody thought very much of the flowers; neither did I, who had seen it in flower in the Mishmi hills three or four years after finding it in the Tsangpo Gorge. On this later occasion I saw not only the flowers but also the young leaves just emerging from the buds, chubby and bronze-red and furred with soft white hairs. In the Tsangpo Gorge in November the current year's leaves had of course lost their youthfulness. I commended the plant for its foliage, but this had already attracted attention at home, and the plant is prized for it alone. After some delay it was named *Rhododendron exasperatum*—not for its monstrous roughness but because of the worry caused to the botanist who had tried to classify it, and found it less easy than it appeared.

I also spent some little time looking for the capsules of a certain rhododendron with strange smooth-looking, reticulate-veined leaves, only to realize, when failure to find any at last roused my suspicion, that it was not a rhododendron at all! Nor was I the first botanist to waste his time thus.

Near the monastery was a marshy hollow which in summer was a swamp; a prostrate tangle of ascending stems, which reminded me very much of mangrove, half filled it. It proved, however, to be a rhododendron, which came as a surprise—not that I had supposed it *was* mangrove! When in due course this too flowered in England the fine scarlet flowers earned for it the name *Rhododendron venator*—'huntsman'—in allusion to his scarlet coat. In England it grows eight feet high, but at Pemakochung the tangled stems rose no more than three feet above the ground. It belongs to a group which are mostly trees, so that even eight feet is somewhat undersized. *R. venator* is not quite in the top flight, but this has nothing to do with the colour of its flowers—on the contrary, it is a scarlet much sought after by hybridizers. It is fairly hardy, more so than any of its close allies.

However, the best rhododendron found on this memorable day of rest was a dwarf plant growing on the rugged flank of the ridge at the highest point reached. It formed twiggy tuffets, eight or ten inches high and a foot through, with small, pointed leaves, rather crimped by the cold. I could not guess the colour of the flowers, but they were solitary and erect, and numerous. If the colour was good, here was a first-class rock-plant, which might be so covered with flowers as to hide the leaves. Though somewhat shrivelled now, I foresaw a future for it, and collected every capsule I could find—they were very small, and contained (for a rhododendron) few seeds. Thus in due course *Rhododendron pemakoense*—named after the Tibetan province of Pemako, where I collected it—came into cultivation and fulfilled its early promise. Now, over thirty years later, it is one of the most popular rock-garden rhododendrons of the day, not excepting even the much beloved *R. leucaspis*; when well established the rose-purple flowers hide every leaf. It has never been found since.

Next morning we continued our journey through the gorge. Below Pemakochung there was no recognized path, and walking became much more difficult. The men cut a track through the waist-high fern undergrowth and enormous stinging nettles in the general direction pointed out by the guide. They agreed that there had formerly been a track, but it had been out of use for many years, though jungle tribesmen sometimes came this way in the winter. Intermittently they found traces of the old route—a crossing-place over a difficult ravine here, a ladder up a cliff there, sometimes an ancient fireplace at the foot of a tree.

The long delays gave me ample opportunity to collect plants and seeds, as well as to take compass bearings. In the gullies the forest was thicker than ever, but in the open the cliffs were too sheer to support much vegetation, though where cracks occurred, trees wedged themselves in. The so-called ladders were tall trunks, slender as scaffold poles, with notches cut for foothold; they stood on ledges, leaning almost upright against the precipice. My companion found these all in the day's work and went up the slimmest of them without a qualm, carrying a heavy rucksack. But he had been trained in the Navy. I found these notched logs precarious, and shed my load before climbing them fearfully. On one occasion we were forced to halt for an hour to cut and fix a ladder for ourselves. The porters who did this were as agile as monkeys and quite fearless. At other times we found ourselves scrambling over huge rocks at the bottom of the gorge; and when I dropped behind to collect anything the whole party instantly disappeared from view, swallowed up in the awful chaos.

The river here was lined with thickets of rhododendron, including large bushes of *R. megacalyx*, whose pale, beautifully shaped oval leaves, glistening with golden scales, are unmistakable; no less beautiful are the marble-white scented flowers. The presence of this plant showed that we were getting down to lower and warmer levels; however, one night we had to sleep among the rocks, like marmots; rain added to our discomfort. Here, perched on a large flat-topped rock amid a scanty growth of mosses and ferns, a small undershrub rhododendron, not more than a foot high, attracted my attention. It had much the appearance of a genuine dwarf, except that it bore two immense erect capsules, very like those of *R. nuttallii*. I guessed that it had great white trumpet-lily flowers. There, however, I was wrong. The flowers, which first opened in Ireland, though shaped like trumpet lilies, were pale yellow. It was not *R. nuttallii*, which is a much bigger shrub, but was closely related to it, and was named *R. headfortianum* after the Marquis of Headfort, who first flowered it.

Ten days after leaving Pemakochung we veered away from the gorge to cross a high spur, round which the river slewed menacingly out of sight, crashing down fall after fall. It was a steep but not difficult climb to the top; the descent on the other side was tougher. There were said to be takin here, and we found their droppings. The takin, or goat-ox (*Budorcas*—there is only one species), is found at fairly high elevations from the Eastern Himalayas to Szechwan and Shensi. One well-marked variety is found in Bhutan at the western end of its range, and a second well-marked variety in Shensi at the eastern end. It usually lives at about ten thousand feet in the summer, but descends into the river valleys a few thousand feet lower in winter.

At the farther foot of the spur we found ourselves near the river again, in a broader valley, with cultivated terraces and two or three small villages. We were now below the point where the Po-Tsangpo, coming in from the north-east, joins the Kongbo-Tsangpo. From here we worked our way back upstream, crossed the main river by ropeway below the confluence, then crossed the Po-Tsangpo. Finally, after two days' hard climbing, we looked down into the fathomless trench which seems to have been split in the Himalayas, as by a blow, to free the Tsangpo—the river was unbelievably narrow and almost bottomless, the gorge unbelievably deep.

By this time we had descended to the level of big-leafed rhododendrons and magnolias, cherries, blue pines, and other trees abundant in more familiar forests. We crossed a gully where tree rhododendrons with large leaves, whose silvery under-surfaces gleamed like burnished pewter, crowded together. It looked to me almost exactly like *R. sino-grande*, but in the absence of flowers it was impossible to say for certain; and for those we had to wait nearly twenty years. The deep-pink flowers then distinguished it from *R. sino-grande*, its near relation, as botanically (and even more, horticulturally) distinct. It was called *R. mollyanum*—an unfortunate choice which will have to be changed.[1]

Leaving the Kongbo-Tsangpo, we marched through pine-forest up the gorge of the smaller Po-Tsangpo, towards better-known country, continuing as we went to collect seed of rhodo-dendrons, known and unknown, and of other plants. And here I found my last unfamiliar rhododendron, a small tree with sleek leaves. This proved to be, as indeed I expected, unhardy in England. However, it is grown under glass, where its beautiful blush-pink flowers can be seen at their best. Appropriately it is named *R. scopulorum*—"of the crags."

By now winter had stretched forth its icy hand, the wind whistled drearily across the plateau, raising clouds of dust and sand, hiding the sun. But when the wind dropped the air was crisp and exhilarating, the sky was blue, the landscape immeas-urably grand. Even the mighty Tsangpo, in the upper reaches, was fringed with ice. In January, the coldest month of the year, we re-crossed the Himalaya in deep snow and bitter wind; nor was it till we were far down in the warm valleys of western Bhutan and nearing the plains that we saw flowers again.

Without a doubt, our winter journey through the gorge of the Tsangpo had been worth while. The forests of rhododendron,

[1] There is already an Indonesian rhododendron named *R. mollianum*. According to the precise rules of botanical nomenclature, two different species cannot both have the same name. The first one to be named prevails.

climbing up step by step for hundreds, for thousands, of feet to the everlasting snows, were breathtaking. The echoless cliffs hurled the spray of the rushing river high in the air; but the forest quickly muffled and absorbed the sound, and even the wind slunk quietly along, awed by the overwhelming vegetation.

What, then, must it be like in the spring, when forests a mile long and a mile high would be in full bloom, thousands upon thousands of trees in flower together, making huge daubs, mounds, and bands of colour in the dark gorge! I doubt whether we had noticed, in winter, more than half the species which grow here. How they would light up the shadows! It is a spectacle which some future botanical explorer may enjoy, if it is possible to traverse the gorge when the river is in snow spate. No collecting 'blind' for him! No rhododendrons unseen!

· 8 ·

Lilies in the Sun

AT the end of the war I was in Assam. For two years the
U.S. Army Air Force had been flying huge quantities of
military stores to Kunming, over what was called the
Hump. The Hump is simply the rugged jungle-covered country
which lies between India and China, and is sliced from north to
south by the deep gorges cut by many rivers, including the
Irrawaddy, Salween, and Mekong. With this region I am comparatively familiar, as I have spent many years exploring there.

Two or three hundred U.S. aircraft were lost in those fathomless jungles during the long and hazardous operations. Few, if
any, were lost to Japanese fighters; it was mist, rain, and wild
weather among the high mountains that claimed nearly all of
them. It now fell to the lot of the American Air Force to pick
up the remains. All crashes had been located as nearly as possible and marked on the map. Teams were sent out to find them,
and in some cases to learn where their crews and passengers had
been buried. As I was free just then, I volunteered to help in
the hunt, and was taken on by the Air Force. Several planes lost
between Assam and Burma were assigned to me, and, accompanied by two G.I.'s, I set out for Manipur State.

Leaving the jeep in Ukhrul, we went on foot across a valley
and reached a village farther north. From here, looking across
another deep valley, I saw the peak of Sirhoi Kashong, 8445
feet high. That afternoon I went for a walk up the ridge above
the village, to get a general view over the surrounding mountains.

At about seven thousand feet or a little higher I found myself
on a limestone slope covered with short crisp turf. The track
skirted a scree which lay at the foot of the razor-edged ridge
above, then worked its way up to the crest farther along. It was
winter, and the slope was very bare; yet it was just the sort of

ground I would carefully cast my eyes over in the hope of noticing some unusual plant. I did so, and presently—not a little to my surprise—I saw the open capsule of a dwarf iris. It was almost certainly *Iris kamaonensis*, a widespread species; but I was delighted to see it because it evoked happy memories and also suggested greater possibilities. I redoubled my efforts as I went along. It was getting dark; I must hurry if I wanted to find anything more. I scrambled up the steep face above the scree, which brought the ground closer to my eyes, and near the top I found more iris, and traces of other plants, but nothing outstanding.

We had already finished our work on the plane which had crashed in the pine forest not far from here, and by this time were on our way back to Ukhrul. The direct route was by a track which crossed the deep valley to the Sirhoi ridge. With my two companions I set out next morning. It was a warm January day, the path was steep, and the distance farther than it looked. Towards evening, having crossed the valley, we found ourselves on the ridge which led to the top of Sirhoi, with the village still some distance away but in the opposite direction. I was tired myself; my young companions seemed almost at their last gasp. Men accustomed to going everywhere on wheels tire quickly on foot; to have to toil up and down steep hillsides by a scarcely visible track, on a hot day, was not their idea of Army life. They lagged behind. However, we eventually reached a rest-house beyond the village, ate our evening meal out of a tin, and flung ourselves down on our bedding-rolls to sleep.

Next day the choice seemed to be between returning to Ukhrul by the bridle-path, or taking another day to go to the top of Sirhoi and back to see what we could see, returning to Ukhrul the day after. I was strongly in favour of the latter course, but the G.I.'s whose feet were already blistered, were just as strongly against it. Had I insisted on their accompanying me no doubt they would have made an attempt to do so. But actually our allotted task was done, and it was a piece of rather gratuitous exercise to go to the top of Sirhoi, the highest mountain in East Manipur, just to see if there was any wreckage up there. I decided to go myself, but there was no necessity to drag the G.I.'s along too. I therefore asked them to follow the bridle-path to Ukhrul, taking it very easily, load up the jeep, and wait for me. I expected to arrive early the following morning, so that we could start back immediately and reach Imphal, forty-five miles distant, the same evening.

We were up early, and after breakfast our ways parted. With two local men I set out for the summit, and we were soon ascending steeply through dull second growth where formerly there had been forest. Then came a traverse through untouched forest, till, emerging into the open, a sharp ascent brought us to the crest of the ridge at an altitude of about seven thousand feet.

I noticed immediately a clear-cut division into the forest on one side of the ridge, and short grass on the exposed south side. The sharp contrast was in part artificial, since the grass was maintained by annual burning. The object of this was not for grazing stock but to entice deer and other game out of the forest into the open. Rock and gravel frequently showed through the turf, and on these threadbare patches grew the same dwarf iris from which I gleaned a few seeds.

But now I found something far more exciting. This was another trilocular top-shaped capsule, which could only be that of a lily (or possibly, I thought, a Nomocharis, which may be briefly described as an alpine lily). Yet it was almost too low down for a Nomocharis; there was nothing really alpine about this mountain, in spite of turf and scree. The plant was barely six inches high, and it bore a solitary terminal capsule about the size of *Nomocharis pardanthina*. I dug it up—a difficult job in that hard rocky soil—and three inches below the surface I found a small whitish bulb. The dry crumbling fruit, and several others on plants growing near by, contained a few leather-brown seeds which the wind had failed to dislodge. They would probably remain till the thin walls of the capsule were soaked and rotted by the summer rain, to be incorporated with the mould; or they might germinate within the capsule itself.

As I expected, the plant was more abundant higher up, and I found a fair number, very few of which contained seeds. But I gathered enough to have a good chance of raising it, for the seeds were plump and obviously fertile. I also dug up a few bulbs to send to my friend the Political Agent for Manipur State in Imphal, who was a keen gardener. It would be asking a lot of this lily—if it was a lily—to grow in the Residency garden on the hot plains five thousand feet below, but at any rate it was worth trying. Other bulbs I sent to Mrs Holder, a famous gardener living in Shillong and an old friend. The seeds went to the

Royal Horticultural Society. And so back with my footsore
G.I.'s to Imphal and the Assam valley, when my assignment
with the American Air Force ended.

Early that summer my plant flowered in the Residency garden
in Imphal. The annual rainfall on the Imphal plain is barely
fifty inches—much less than in the Assam valley. It happened
to be a particularly hot spring with a long drought, and nothing
could have been worse for any lily. Nevertheless it flowered.
When later I asked the Resident, Mr C. Gimson, to give me an
appreciation, or a description of it, he was a little scathing. He
wrote that he had hardly noticed it; so far as he remembered,
the flowers were small, almost insignificant; anyway he was not
impressed, and had forgotten about them. Perhaps the colour
was best described as—dirty white!

Mrs Holder's bulbs also flowered the first year, and her report
was just as damning as Gimson's. I was indignant. Dirty white
indeed! Why, no lily could possibly be that! Anyhow it wasn't
a fair test. The climate of Imphal is very different from that at
7500 feet up in the hills and the plant couldn't be expected to
do itself justice in the middle of a heat-wave.

In the spring of 1947 I returned to England. The Director of
the New York Botanic Garden had invited me to collect plants
for the gardens of California and the Southern States, and I had
to consider where would be a good place to go. I thought of
going to the hills of South India, which have a rich flora including many shrubs likely to be of horticultural value; but there
was little indication whether they would prove hardy in California—the Nilgiri and Palni hills are well inside the tropics.
After my visit to Ukhrul, however, I decided that Manipur might
be a more promising region for hardy plants. It was sufficiently
unexplored to be worth a whole-time expedition, and there was
no previous record of any lily there.

Before leaving Assam I heard in a letter from the Royal
Horticultural Society that the seeds of my problem plant had
germinated well, and shortly after my return to England one
flowered under glass. I did not see it, I was too busy. Dr Turrill,
of Kew, identified it as definitely a lily and thought it was
probably a new species. Before describing and naming it, however, he wanted to see more material, preferably living plants.
Those raised from seed had so far produced only one flower.

"What was it like?" I asked.

"Well, it wasn't very impressive, but of course . . ."

"What colour was it?"

He looked thoughtful. "Oh, you might call it a sort of dingy white! " he said, after a pause.

It was enough. Could anything be more damning! Nothing extenuate, nor set down aught in malice, I thought. It was as though the plant had a millstone tied round its neck from birth.

Bitterly disappointed as I was, I did not lose faith in my Manipur lily, though I had nothing but a hunch to go on. Raised from both seed and bulb, the plant had proved dismal; but I consoled myself with the reflection that the Wisley plant had been forced under glass, and could no more do itself justice than could the Imphal plants in a heat-wave. If I found the wild plant in flower, growing under natural conditions, we should see! (Of Mrs Holder's plants, grown only two thousand feet below their normal altitude, I preferred not to think at all. It was so hard to find a satisfactory excuse for them!)

Six months later, at the end of 1947, my wife and I sailed for India.

The long train journey from Bombay across India might be described as uneventful. The longer—in time—journey from Calcutta across Bengal to Jorhat, in Assam, was rather less so, as there were complications on the internal frontiers of the New India, particularly when we had to change trains in the middle of the night. However, we reached our destination safely. At least the trains did run.

Eventually we reached Imphal; and before the end of February we were back in Ukhrul. Early as it was, two beautiful trees were in full bloom. One of them was the carmine cherry (*Prunus cerasoides rubea*), the other a crab-apple (*Pyrus pashia*) —both of them were common. Snow-white pyramids of apple-blossom lit up the forest everywhere—they looked like arc-lights. The forest canopy itself was a mosaic of many colours, olive-green, emerald, wine-red, silver, and gold, as thousands of twinkling leaf-buds opened and fledged the forest anew. Across the valley Sirhoi loomed sombre and colourless, its brow two thousand feet higher than the Ukhrul ridge.

Towards the end of April we judged it time to see if the lily was coming up, and set out for Sirhoi. Seen from a distance, the mountain had slightly changed colour in places, and a tinge of green had appeared on its bare slopes. We camped at the site where I and my G.I.'s had slept two-and-a-half years previously, and on a lovely spring day walked to the top, taking about four hours from the village. Of the dwarf iris we saw no trace, except for an occasional crumbling capsule, but the lily was coming up. No plant was yet more than an inch or two high, a rosette of leaves almost flush with the ground; but on one of these we counted seven flower-buds, packed like eggs in a green nest. This was as much as I had expected to see. We dug up half a dozen bulbs and carried them back, to plant by our cottage in Ukhrul.

White rhododendrons (*R. johnstoneanum*) were in full bloom along the edge of the forest. They made a beautiful display, especially some growing on an open landslip which were heavily flushed with pink. Their charm was further increased by their sweet fragrance.

So the reconnaissance for the Manipur lily proved successful. It was now only a matter of "watch and pray."

In May we went on tour with the object of ascending Hkayam Bum, a mountain about 9300 feet high some distance to the east, near the Burma frontier. Here we hoped to find more rhododendrons. It turned out to be an exceptionally wet month, with much heavy rain and wind, which made collecting—and even finding plants at all in the forest—very difficult. Towards the end of the tour we became impatient to see how our lilies at Ukhrul were doing. I had an idea they might be in flower by now. We made the usual stages, but on the last day hurried on ahead of the coolies.

The long pull of three miles up the last hill to the Ukhrul ridge was behind us; we almost ran along the level path to the cottage, and went straight to the tiny strip of prepared soil by the entrance. This had been fenced against marauding pigs; cattle, however, put their heads over the fence and browsed the tops off any plants they fancied. The lilies were in flower—or rather, had flowered—but were more than half over; only one complete flower and several fragmentary ones remained. They were not tall enough to be eaten by the cattle, but heavy raindrops had made little craters in the soil and spattered the plants with mud from head to foot. They looked bedraggled, homesick, woebegone, and cheap. Their colour? Well—muddy white describes it!

I was shocked and disappointed, but I rallied later. The final test had still to come: the Manipur lily, growing on its own ground, in its own time.

Could excuses be found for our Ukhrul plants too? The weather?—but it had been no better on Sirhoi, which had been smothered in cloud for five weeks. Twelve or fifteen hundred feet difference of altitude?—negligible! Well then, the sour, unappetizing village soil and the juvenile plants?—but the bulbs had been carried down in the clods of Sirhoi turf that originally enclosed them!

Whatever the reason, I *still* felt that these miserable lilies were not the real thing. What seemed certain was that it was now in full bloom on Sirhoi, and that if we wanted to see the lily at its best we must go soon.

At the end of May the weather changed, and June ushered in a succession of radiant days, warm, sunny, and fragrant with the scent of flowers. But coolies were not to be had for love or money; the entire population of the village was at work in the rice-fields from dawn to dusk; it was the transplanting season, and their lives depended on the rice crop. It was therefore not possible to camp on Sirhoi this time, but it was quite possible to walk there and back in a day. All we wanted was to see the lilies growing wild, and to collect specimens to press and describe in detail. By June 4 we had made up our minds, and the long walk was fixed for the next day.

It was pleasant walking in the grey coolness of the dawn, when the grass was drenched with dew and the sharmas were singing sweetly before the heat drove all the birds into the shade of the forest. We covered the miles fast, and long before midday were well up on the ridge. Although we had come primarily to see the lily, there were many other interesting plants in flower which we could not ignore, so we had to slow down. As soon as we reached the turf slope at about seven thousand feet, where I had found the first lily capsule two-and-a-half years previously, we began quartering the ground.

A few hundred feet higher we found the first flower, and stood before it spellbound. I could have laughed aloud, but it would have been sacrilege, like laughing in church. Dirty white? dingy white? muddy white? What rubbish! The half-nodding bell was a delicate shell-pink outside, like dawn in June, with the sheen of watered silk; inside, it was like faintly flushed alabaster. The points of the petals curled back, but towards the base clasped one another closely. The stamens too were beautiful; the anthers, with their deep honey-orange pollen, are so nicely balanced on the needle-tips of the filaments that they tremble at a touch. We sang, we shouted with joy; then moved on, up the hill, up the hill, up the hill, till we found ourselves surrounded by pink lilies in bud, lilies half open, lilies in full bloom. There were stems with two, with three, flowers; and as we approached the summit, where in sheltered hollows the grass grew longer, we found them as much as three feet high, each stem bearing six or eight flowers. The long pointed damask-rose buds added a special charm. When a breeze swept through the meadow, hundreds of lilies bowed their heads and swung their bells to and fro, the whole slope twinkling and dancing joyfully.

There was no need to mark plants for seed. There were thousands of lilies—but just on this *one* mountain. We saw it nowhere else, not even on an almost equally high grassy hilltop only a few miles distant. By the time we had spent six hours searching for, collecting, and pressing plants, taking photographs, walking among the lilies as in a dream, the day was far spent. Already the sun was sinking down towards the western hills.

But the walk back was memorable too. We trod on air, filled with the quiet satisfaction of something done, a piece of work completed. We sang snatches of song. The sun set, the short dusk deepened, and we began to grow weary. At the foot of the last hill, with twenty-two miles behind us and three more still to go, a voice hailed us from a thicket, and there beside the path was our Naga cook, Mangalay. Realizing that by the time we reached the foot of the ridge we should be feeling exhausted, he had brought down a kettle, tea, milk, mugs, everything. Then he lit a fire, boiled some water, and sat down to wait for us. When he heard us singing on the path above he made the tea, and appeared before us like a jin. The pot stood warm and inviting beside the blazing logs. How we blessed him as we drank cup after cup of foaming tea. We dared not stay long though, or we should soon grow too stiff to move. But presently we were covering the last three miles like giants refreshed.

So at last the Manipur lily justified itself.

In July we went again to the top of Sirhoi, camping for a fortnight while it rained and rained. I thought the lily would

Rhododendron vellereum is a very slow-growing tree. This one, in Kongbo, South-east Tibet, is probably at least fifty years old

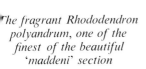

The fragrant Rhododendron polyandrum, one of the finest of the beautiful 'maddeni' section

In the heart of the Tsangpo Gorge, Tibet, a mighty river sculptures the living rock

Though only a tributary of the great Tsangpo, the Gyamda River is totally unnavigable

long have been over, but it wasn't. There were not now hundreds of flowers, but there were still dozens, late-comers all, and, if possible, beaded as they now were with silver rain-drops, they were even more beautiful than in June. On south slopes all were tiny plants a few inches high, flowering perhaps for the first time; they seemed to be of a deeper pink than I remembered, and they had an unexpected careless graciousness about them. It was rapture to be among them again. One of the points which struck me forcibly was the very considerable difference between plants growing on the sheltered side of the hill and those on the south face fully exposed to wind and sun. Here and there, even on the sheltered slope, forest did not reach quite to the crest of the ridge; there would be a small bay with a protecting wall of forest round three sides of it where the grass grew long. It was in such places that I had found plants three and even four feet high, bearing up to six or eight flowers. I have already mentioned a plant which in April bore seven buds.

All along the crest of the ridge, where a rank growth of tall grass and prickly shrubs marked the transition from turf to forest, there were a few stalwart lilies growing just over the brow. But as the proportion of meadow on the shaded side was very small compared with the large areas of turf on the open side, so also tall plants were few compared with the hundreds of almost dwarf plants bearing one or two flowers only. That the Manipur lily grows on both sides—that is to say, in full sun and in half shade—in itself suggests a certain degree of adaptability. It would certainly be worth while to try it in several positions in the garden. One fact emerges: it will not stand drought or near-drought conditions in the growing season. Even direct sunlight slightly bleaches the flowers. I am told it does best on a north slope, in England.

It was autumn when we visited Sirhoi for the fourth and last time, camping near the summit. There were still a few late flowers in the long grass, the most conspicuous being the blue spires of monkshood. Everywhere the lily capsules were swollen with ripe seed. We dug up bulbs too, selecting the best to send home by air. They arrived in good condition, and Sir Frederick Stern planted them in pots immediately in a cool house.

From this point on, with mature bulbs growing well in the open, one could safely prophesy triumphant progress for the Manipur lily (now named *Lilium mackliniae* for my wife) in the gardens of England. But success was not immediate—perhaps lasting success never is. Its promising career met with a severe check at the outset, when the first plants were shown at the Chelsea Flower Show. The normal flowering-time for this lily, grown in the open in the south of England, is July; and the Chelsea Show comes at the end of May. The plants had therefore to be forced under glass, which did them no good. They flowered and were shown, surrounded by the finest lilies in the country. Naturally they failed to stand up to the test, and to complete their discomfiture the heat in the crowded marquee on a hot day was too much for them altogether; they wilted. After that sorry introduction the Manipur lily was in temporary eclipse, except for the discerning. In July it flowered naturally in England and was acclaimed by Sir Frederick Stern and other lily specialists.

Recently an experienced and far-sighted nurseryman wrote these words of it: "With accumulating experience there seems every reason to believe that the exquisitely lovely Manipur lily is to be a first-rate garden plant." And that, written by an expert, of a plant thrice damned, is praise indeed.

·9·

Interlude for Gentians

FEW rock-plants give the alpine gardener more unalloyed delight than gentians. Those who have the necessary cunning, or luck, to grow successfully such aristocrats as *Gentiana sino-ornata*, *Gentiana hexaphylla*, *Gentiana farreri*, and *Gentiana veitchiorum* are greatly envied by their less gifted or less fortunate gardening friends who cannot. Yet, out of over eight hundred species[1] known from the temperate regions and tropical mountain-tops of the world, fewer than 10 per cent. are in general cultivation; probably fewer than 10 per cent. are worth cultivating. Not all gentians are the ultra-blue trumpet flowers we admire so much, and it is a waste of time trying to persuade ourselves that geese are swans. The mere fact that a plant is the scion of a noble family carries no assurance that it is in itself noble.

Gentians of the Ornata group belonging to the section Frigida (which includes all the finest of the mat-forming Sino-Himalayan species, such as those just referred to) must be seen in flower to be believed; one might say, *can* be seen only in flower. Earlier in the season, if visible above ground at all, they are wizened, weedy-looking little alpines, unimpressive to the last degree. Nearly all are high alpines, and spend at least half their lives in darkness, either underground or under the snow. They hardly begin to show above ground before July. Then, under the stimulus of a hot sun, warm rain, and longer daylight, they grow fast. In the autumn they flower gloriously. It seems rather

[1] This number is taken from David Wilkie, the authority on the genus. Wilkie, in his excellent work *Gentians*, includes a large number of plants now transferred to the genus Gentianella, or to other genera. Some botanists admit only about two hundred species of true Gentiana, including three British species.

curious that the melting of the snow in May and June has no visible effect on these alpine gentians.

In Europe one visits the Alps or other central European mountain ranges in June to see gentians in flower, though some of the less patrician species flower later. It is in June that *Gentiana verna* and the so-called *acaulis* gentians, coming into flower as the snow recedes, are found at their best. In Britain and Ireland *verna* flowers in May. But in the Himalayas and adjoining mountains of Assam, Burma, and Yunnan, September is too early; one must go in October, or even in November, to see gentians of the Ornata type as they really should be seen.

The reason for their tardy appearance must be that, though they would like to behave as their relations in the mountains of Europe behave, they find themselves in a quandary. In the Himalayan spring they are still under the snow; to produce flowers they need direct sunlight, and lots of it. But by the time the snow has melted the monsoon has broken, the sun disappeared. For months the skies are grey, and there are very few bright intervals indeed. The gentians can do nothing but go underground and await the sun. At the same time they build up their reserves.

At last, in October, the rains begin to slacken, there are more and longer sunny periods, the heavy monsoon clouds decrease, disperse, dissolve. And suddenly, in the midst of their rejoicing, the gentians discover that autumn is half gone and that winter is only just round the corner. But by now the nights are cold, with sharp frosts, the wind has an edge to it, the daylight is shorter by one or two hours; and as winter relentlessly approaches these conditions are all intensified. True, the sunshine is bright and lasting. But the waning sun is lower in the sky and has little warmth before noon, while the light is pale and yellow.

So the alpine gentians make a wild rush for it and leap into flower, all together, in one gorgeous explosion of colour. Cold does not wither them, nor darkness dim their infinite variety. Warmed by the midday sun, they all flower at once in mad and merry exhilaration, and before the end of October the crisp and frosty lawns are dappled blue with them; in the early morning sunlight the flowers glitter as though the dome of heaven itself had cracked and fallen in a shower of splinters. Then, as the earth is faintly warmed by the sun's rays, the hoar-frost melts, and the crystallized flowers relax, only to stiffen again after sunset.

Meanwhile the thong-like roots, striking out in all directions, probe deep into the dry soil for moisture, though they must take up only minute quantities. But October frosts hardly penetrate beneath the surface.

From the day I first saw *G. sino-ornata* growing above Atuntzu, in Yunnan, to the day in November 1956 when I saw the Cambridge-blue gentian on the summit of Mount Victoria, in Burma, I have been bewitched by these incomparable rock-plants. And I have seen many of them, growing under various conditions and in many places. Among them were *G. veitchiorum* and *G. szechenyii* in Tibet, *G. gilvostriata* and *G. setulifolia* in North Burma, *G. hexaphylla* and *G. trichotoma* in China, and *G. amoena* and others in the Himalayas. These, and their hybrids, are the plants which every rock gardener hopes to grow, and it is of success or failure with these that we read in the gardening Press.

As a plant-hunter I am inclined to think that all the really first-class gentians of Sino-Himalaya have been found, and that no more species remain to be discovered by the next generation. There may be distinct (but hardly better) varieties, not yet introduced, and it may be remarked that *G. setulifolia* is a species which has never been in cultivation.

But gentians do not generally hide their light under a bushel; not gentians of the Frigida section at any rate. Primulas may lurk and smirk behind rocks; but gentians—no; they grow boldly out in the open, and are easily seen in flower, though not at any other time. They do not lurk under cover, or hide in deep gorges which are like subterranean passages in that they have to be explored yard by yard.

Now, in the alps of Sino-Himalaya, in the fine weather, visibility is exceptionally good. One can see not only for great distances, but with great clarity. If you rake a large slice of grassland with the eye of a sniper, aided by a good field-glass, anything as blue as a gentian shines like a star at dusk, growing brighter while you look. Few can have been missed during the last fifty years. If you would find a new gentian you must first find some new country; and, even more important, be there at the right time.

Nor do Ornata gentians, as a rule, grow in solitary state. They are sociable plants, and enjoy the company of their own kind. On the breezy grasslands of the Tibetan plateau they form extensive though uncrowded colonies. Here the rainfall is moderate, but certain; the snowfall dependable and prolonged; and the winter cold severe. This is a combination of weather that makes it the more surprising we should be able to grow any of these gentians in our gardens. The rainfall at least is right in England, but even that generally comes with us at the wrong time. As for our snow, if it comes at all, it always comes when least expected by the innocent gardener, and generally *where* least expected too. It is against these odds that the Ornata gentians in our midst must struggle. Their innate, deep-seated rhythm carries them bravely along for several years, while they ride the shocks, and flower faithfully in the autumn; but it is not surprising that some lack the nimble constitution necessary for quick and frequent adjustment, and succumb. Gardeners then write them down as short-lived.

However, a few species of Frigida gentian grow on the rain-sodden mountains of North Burma and the Eastern Himalaya. They too are entombed beneath the snow for months, flowering in the bright but short autumn, just before the heavy snow comes. They are painfully difficult to cultivate.

But though there may be no more—certainly very few—first-class gentians to be discovered in Sino-Himalaya, not all of those known are in cultivation. Except for G. *setulifolia*, already mentioned, most of them have been—but several are now lost—including G. *szechenyii*. How many gardeners have ever seen it? G. *wardii*, with flowers of an almost iridescent soap-bubble blue (which suggested the baby name "blue bubble" for this species), has never been in cultivation either. Though not an Ornata gentian, it ranks as an equal. It is a mat plant growing at high altitudes in North Burma among scattered Pleurogynes, saxifrages, and Swertias. The outspread conical blue flowers look like limpets stuck to ice-graved rocks.

The trouble with gentians is that, though they are plants of a temperate climate, they are really alpines first and temperate plants afterwards; and alpines are never easy. Even in Britain, where the climate is surely temperate, and cool temperate at that, they are mostly plants of the hills. Most of the British lowland species we used to call Gentiana are now called Gentianella, leaving us only three real gentians of our own, *GG. pneumonanthe, verna*, and *nivalis*. Yet though they have changed their names, the others have not changed their appearance.

It is a wonderful experience to come suddenly on colonies of gentian in full bloom. When the colour of rhododendrons has gone from the hills a grass slope bestrewn with large clumps of gentian is a sight to be for ever cherished and remembered.

I shall never forget first seeing *G. sino-ornata* growing wild. It was on a steep mountain-side of loose hungry-looking scree soil, with lots of stones, and many scattered bushes; and I came on it unexpectedly. The ascent was steep and rather tiresome, as I kept slipping; but it was the first time I had tried this route and I thought it might be worth while to persevere. When at last I came to the first gentians, deep blue with that hint of violet that you get on a sunny morning in the South China Sea, I felt it had indeed been worth while; the form and colour made an indelible impression.

At that time the plant had already been introduced into England, but it had not yet attained the immense popularity it enjoys to-day. Even then I thought it without a peer among rock-plants. I was ambitious to discover a rival to it, but several years passed before I found *Gentiana gilvostriata*. In most points this species might have competed with *G. sino-ornata*, but it proved just a little more difficult, and has never attained real popularity. Though well-established, it is still a plant for the expert rock gardener. *G. gilvostriata* grows on the great snow range of North Burma, where the climate is more cruel than that of Tibet itself, and much less dry.

G. veitchiorum is another plant I admire greatly. I saw it growing in large clumps over a wide wet pasture where yak, retiring down an alpine valley to the village below as the short summer drew to a close, rested and grazed for a few last days. At that time Lord Cranbrook and I were exploring the sources of the Irrawaddy, finding unexpected glaciers and unguessed rivers. We had just crossed a difficult pass of over fifteen thousand feet—one side of it was a dead glacier—and we were surprised to find ourselves approaching so large a river system, all glacier water too. We seemed to be surrounded by nameless snow mountains, which, though furrowed by glaciers, were not very high. It was their bulk, and the number of them, rather than their height, which was so surprising. And all round us in the meadow, trampled on by grazing yak, were clumps of gentian, their great blue trumpets gaping to the sky.

An entirely different plant, also from eastern Tibet, is *Gentiana trichotoma*. It bears its light sea-blue flowers in long, slender spikes. A Frigida, though not of the Ornata group, it too grows scattered over the alpine grassland, often in company with *G. szechenyii*, whose inflated goblet-shaped flowers are a curious shade of violet tinged with green, heavily speckled and spotted.

It is difficult to describe what these alpine flowers really look like in their wild surroundings, so small and frail against the immensity of the background. Only in vivid colour and in numbers can they draw attention to themselves; and seen from a short way away, so alike are they in general appearance, that words seem inadequate to distinguish one from another. But even as I write I recall each species with the utmost clarity, for each has a personality of its own, as distinct as two human beings. I remember too the occasion, the very day, when I first found each one, and all the details of the hunt. I live the expedition over again, week by week, month by month, with its triumphs and disappointments, its surprises and trivialities; and always before me are the flowers I found. Perhaps it is those dramatic landscapes, with their rows of jagged peaks and carved valleys, as aloof as the mountains of the moon, that one remembers most clearly; and every one of them associated with a plant.

It was not till 1956 that I found another first-class new gentian. It seemed to have every quality a gentian could have, including colour, size and shape of corolla, habit, mode of growth, and —anonymity. But had it the one indispensable quality—hardiness—without which the rest was vain? It was a very unexpected find, because Mount Victoria, on the western wall of Burma, where it grows, does not reach up to the alpine region. If it were six degrees farther north, its ten thousand feet of altitude, surrounded by higher peaks, would be enough to ensure, if not a complete alpine zone, at least a complete alpine flora. But Mount Victoria is inside the tropics, a little north of twenty-one degrees, and there are no surrounding higher peaks to insulate it and keep it cool. There is no alpine zone; but there *are* a few alpine plants—perhaps as many as fifty species—lodged here, none more peculiarly alpine than the gentian referred to.

It was April, the hot weather in Burma, when we climbed this mountain for the first time. The grass slopes, smarting under the fierce sun, were completely dried up, with many bare patches, and it was difficult indeed to tell what plants had grown there—and might grow again. The fluted slopes were steep, and, in places where cliffs broke through the surface, precipitous. Sometimes the grass struggled with scattered small trees and shrubs; it was generally short, but in some hollows long and matted, though it stood upright; no weight of snow had ever flattened it. Several hundred feet below, where the shallow gullies deepened into ravines, the forest began again.

On a hot sunny day we started up the long ridge. The gnarled and twisted rhododendron-trees—many of them must have been over two centuries old—were domes of scarlet blossom, and one grassy mound was mauve with thousands of *Primula denticulata*. Here and there blue anemones were opening. Nothing else was in flower in the dead grass, and I was eager to discover what plants grew here. Obviously in the rainy season these open slopes would present a very different picture. We could make out a few shrivelled flowers of the 'everlasting' type, but little that was positive. So I began a close survey, lying on my belly, and going over the ground foot by foot.

This scrutiny soon began to yield results, including a dwarf iris, whose capsules stood flush with the scanty earth, and similar skeleton remains of Roscoea. The capsules of both still contained a little seed, though they must have been ripe for months. The iris was the more surprising of the two, for the capsules open widely, at ground level, whereas the soft fruits of Roscoea lie below the surface and are further protected by the broad bases of the leaves, which wrap tightly round them. But many Roscoea plants were drifting freely on the hillside, having been snapped off below ground level, the ovary still intact.

It was while collecting Roscoea plants, pinching the base of each to feel whether the capsule contained seeds, that I found the first gentian plants, also adrift. Others were still rooted where they grew, dead and colourless like parchment. But underground the rootstock must have been very much alive, like the honeycombed grey seeds at the bottom of the long beaked capsule. It was rather extraordinary how the capsules of these two plants, so different in all other respects, behaved alike at seed-time, carefully preserving the last seeds. No doubt they would be washed out and planted when the rains came. Thus a succession of sowings over a period of months is assured.

I collected all the gentian plants I could find, stuffing them into a spongebag; and the final result was a pinch of smoke-grey seed at the bottom of the bag. The Roscoea gave a rather better yield of seed, but not so good as the dwarf iris.

When next I saw the summit ridge of Mount Victoria two months later the rains had been going full-blast for five weeks, and the grass slopes facing south were emerald-green, and brilliant with flowers. Very prominent now was Roscoea, only a few inches high, each plant capped by a single (rarely by two) large deep-purple flower, which open in succession. They looked very like orchids. Where they grew thickly there were always to be seen several milk-white blooms; a larger proportion of albinos than I should have expected.

Another abundant meadow-plant was a Polygonum with long, solid poker heads of crowded pink flowers, while here and there were patches of blue iris—though, strangely enough, they were much taller than those of which I had obtained seed in April. Possibly they were a different species. However, these only revealed themselves when they opened to greet an occasional gleam of sunshine.

The mountain was smothered in mist, which came sweeping heavily like wet smoke over the ridge. It was a rather eerie sensation following the narrow path into the dim, dripping forest and out on to the open hillside again, in the teeth of the wind, always wondering what might loom round the next corner. One brushed knee-deep through high grass, and waist-deep through the sodden bushes. Nevertheless I was rather surprised at the lack of flowers on the grass slopes. Had I expected too much? I had certainly expected more.

Several small basins, lined with hard, cracked mud in April, were now ponds; but there were no aquatic plants.

In the middle of October we camped on Mount Victoria for the last time, to collect seed of the spring-flowering plants. I was agog to find the big gentian, fearing we might have just missed it in flower. But even at the beginning of November, by which time the rains had abated, I could see no sign of it. But if the gentian wasn't in flower, everything else was. Rarely have I seen such masses of flowers all along the ridge, most of them in deep drifts, such as golden saxifrage and purple Swertia. One spot, carpeted with thousands of saxifrages, we named the Golden Gully.

It was on November 5 that, along the summit ridge of Mount Victoria, we at last found the first shy gentian-flowers. What a moment that was! So far as appearances went, the flowers were everything I had prayed for—large and trumpet-shaped, a little smaller, perhaps, than those of *G. sino-ornata*, in shape more like those of *G. szechenyii*, to which the plant was obviously related.

But it was the wonderful colour which riveted our gaze. Slowly we took it in, from the wide band of pure Cambridge blue round the top, fading towards the base, to where the corolla is speckled with blue, green, and violet lights. The overall effect is that of a shining China-blue goblet.

Within the next week plants, always prostrate, were coming into flower everywhere between 8500 and ten thousand feet; where the grass was short, or the ground bare and rocky, this miraculous gentian grew abundantly, becoming daily more conspicuous as fresh flowers continued to open. Plants with fifteen or twenty blooms were by no means rare; they must have been eight or ten years old.

On the last day we dug up some flowering plants, hacking out solid lumps of dry earth containing the long roots (so the plant could be increased by division). These were carried down in baskets, packed among layers of deep moss.

Three weeks later, after being twice unpacked and soaked in the sun for a few days, they were unpacked in Rangoon. It was for the last time, before being finally packed for the journey to Europe by air. Several of the plants were still in fine bloom, looking little the worse for their ordeal. We laid them out on the cold stone floor of the bungalow, to gloat over the glorious display and show them proudly to every one who came to see us.

I should think it unlikely that gentians have ever been seen flowering in Rangoon before!

·10·

An Introduction to Slipper Orchids

SLIPPER ORCHIDS are in a class apart; in fact, some botanists put them in a family of their own, the Cypripediaceae. This is not a mere botanical convention; anyone can see that they are quite different from other orchids. We call our very rare *Cypripedium calceolus* lady's slipper. Americans call their beautiful *Cypripedium reginae* white wing moccasin flower; and no doubt there are some equally picturesque names for these startling flowers in Asia, where most of them are found.

One of the first plants I collected on my very first plant-hunt, in Yunnan, was a slipper orchid, *Cypripedium luteum*. It had chrome-yellow flowers with the cool glaze of Chinese porcelain, and broad leaves all the way up the stem. I found it growing in woodland on a steep hillside, well protected from the sun at any rate, and from wind. The altitude was about eleven thousand feet, so one would expect it to be hardy in England. Perhaps it is, but unfortunately it is too difficult to keep. Possibly the mycorrhiza (the fungus which lives in association with the roots of the orchid) provided for it is the wrong kind. Possibly the right kind of mycorrhiza is not hardy in England, or cannot be obtained. Possibly—many things. Whatever the reason, the Chinese yellow slipper orchid does not do well in this country. I doubt whether you would find a single plant of it to-day. I am sorry for that. It is a beautiful orchid, with flowers of unusual charm and delicious colour. The habit is very different from the stiff aristocratic stance of the slipper orchids on the show-stands, which have an air at once prim and ostentatious, like the *nouveau riche*.

A little higher up the hill, that same memorable day, not under trees but on open grass slopes, the floppier *Cypripedium tibeticum* grew in scattered clumps. The flowers are the colour of dried blood, and the large lip is baggy as an old trouser leg, not streamlined as a lady's slipper should be. You would look in vain for this plant in all but a few British gardens, although you might find both *C. calceolus* and *C. reginae*. I have come across *C. tibeticum* several times since that day; but *C. luteum* I saw only once more, twenty-two years later.

Thus was I introduced to slipper orchids in the temperate mountains of Asia.

Slipper orchids have to be searched for, especially when they grow in the jungle. They do not display themselves. They are not conspicuous for size or for their dazzling colours, nor do they grow in such massed battalions that you cannot miss them. They are not sought out by birds of brilliant plumage, by inquisitive mammals, or even by hordes of noisy insects, which, assailing the ear, might lead you to them. They are not easy to see, whether in or out of flower, and can easily be missed.

Some years ago, when I was again in Yunnan, I went home a new way. I wanted to cross the narrow gap between the eastern end of the Himalayas and the beginning of the alps of Yunnan; briefly, from the Yangtze to the Irrawaddy. Through this gap the rivers of southern Tibet, drawn together from a thousand miles and pinched up until they are almost one, pour their waters to open up the breach the glaciers have made. Starting from the Yangtze, I went due west—or as due as the rugged nature of the country would allow—across the mountains and across the Tibetan rivers Mekong and Salween, till I reached the head-waters of the Irrawaddy. Before turning south I crossed these sundered streams also; first, the Taron, which is the eastern Irrawaddy, and the swiftest, deepest, and widest of them all; then the Tazu and Dablu, which are small tributaries; the Tamai, nearly as large as the Taron, the Tisang—again a small tributary, and finally the Mali Hka itself, which is the western Irrawaddy. The entire journey from river to river took about five weeks, three of which were spent within the Irrawaddy watershed. It was early winter and the weather was fine, with only token snow on the high passes; they would be uncrossable by January.

It was in the last few days, shortly before I reached the banks of the Mali Hka and turned south, that by chance I found a remarkable slipper orchid. We had toiled up the long slope from the flat valley of the Tisang—a tributary of the Mali Hka—to the top of the divide. The last few hundred feet were steep, and I halted a short distance below the crest to draw breath. Staring into the forest, not looking for anything in particular, I noticed a number of large scattered rocks. Suddenly my eye lit on a plant with leaves mottled and blotched like a python, light sea-green and dark seaweed-green, from between which sprang an erect stem ending in a single glossy flower. It was unmistakably an orchid, a slipper orchid. The dominant colour is green, heavily overlaid with purple spots, especially on the long lateral petals; they are fringed also with curly purple hairs, which give a pink shadow round the edges of the petals. But the broad upper petal is almost Nile green, with darker curved lines. Column and streamlined lip too are a deeper green, the latter finely or heavily speckled purple.

I saw only a single flower, and collected it. Then I tossed it into the collecting-basket I carried. The basket was already nearly full, but I crammed the orchid in. Alas, when we reached camp a couple of hours later nothing remained of it but a tattered and mutilated corolla. It was torn to shreds, and really there was nothing left to press. Thus a promising orchid was lost to my collection that year. But I never forgot where it grew. Some day I might return and find it again.

Most perennial herbs come up again in the same place year after year, in accordance with a long-established rhythm. But this simple rhythm does not apply to ground orchids. Whether they grow in England, in Burma, or anywhere else, their rhythm is irregular, because they are not entirely self-supporting. They depend in part on a fungus which grows among the roots, hence the general term for these root fungi, mycorrhiza. Without it they cannot grow at all. For several years they may be found in numbers in one particular spot, flowering at the appointed season, neither increasing nor dwindling much in numbers, behaving like rational perennials. Then suddenly they disappear completely, for no apparent reason. Hence with ground orchids it is not just a matter of choosing the right season to find them in flower, but of choosing the right year too; nor is there any warning when their time may come. It seems you may walk over ground where for a decade a species of slipper orchid has flowered annually, and not find one, because all have now gone underground. They may not reappear for years. They may never reappear.

No doubt I was in luck that winter when I marched from the

Yangtze to the Irrawaddy. Two or three days before reaching the plain of Hkamti Long I had halted at the top of the range and stared into the jungle. There I saw the green-and-purple slipper orchid, as described. It was the only one in flower, so far as I could see—perhaps the only one in sight. Was this its first appearance here, or its last? Was it on its way in, or out? I did not know.

Four years passed before I went that way again, but in the reverse direction. I wanted to explore the upper Nam Tamai. I had crossed this river, second only to the Taron, on my journey from the Yangtze. Now I would follow it northward into the mists.

It was already April when I reached the place where I had first seen the slipper orchid. Four months too late. I saw nothing.

Another four or five years passed. Then once again, with Lord Cranbrook, I was drawn irresistibly to the headwaters of the Irrawaddy, and retraced my steps to the Nam Tamai. Crossing the Mali-Tisang divide north-east of Hkamti Long just after Christmas, I went straight to the spot where the slipper orchid grew. To my delight I found the rocks thickly covered with the mottled leaves; a large and flourishing colony had sprung up where eight years ago I had seen only an early pioneer. You couldn't miss them. Many plants were in bud, a few in flower, and I was able to prepare some good specimens and complete my earlier field notes.

Eleven months later, when I passed the place for the fourth time, on our way back to Hkamti Long, the colony was flowering magnificently. I dug up a few dozen plants and pressed more specimens. The living plants were packed in moss, in bamboo baskets, and sewn up in cotton cloth, then posted to England by sea. They were out of the ground for two months. Cypripediums have no pseudobulbs in which to store water, so it was no small triumph that several of them lived to flower at Kew. The hitherto unknown plant was now named *Paphiopedilum wardii* by Mr V. S. Summerhayes, and figured in colour in the *Botanical Magazine*, Vol. 160, t. 9481 (1937); it has an alternative name *Cypripedium wardianum*.

Six more years passed, and again I found myself on the old familiar trail—'the trail that is always new.' For the botanist it is inexhaustible. Once more it was December. However, this time, when I looked to see how my orchid fared, I could not find a single one. The plant had silently and mysteriously disappeared. It should have been in bud and in bloom, so I hardly think I could have failed to notice it, had it been there at all. But three weeks later, across the western Irrawaddy, twenty or thirty miles away as the crow flies, I noticed a few of these plants growing on a shady roadside bank. They could not have been there very long, since none of them were of an age to flower; but the mottled leaves were unmistakable.

This struck me as curious. What had happened? Could my old colony have migrated thirty miles? Hardly—as a colony; though the seeds, light as dust, and lifted and carried by the faintest breeze, could have covered the distance. More probably the original group had either died out or gone underground till better conditions should prevail again, while the new satellite colony had sprung up in the most natural way, as new colonies do. The seed may not have come from the original Mali-Tisang colony at all, but from one much closer, perhaps only a mile away. In any square mile of forest in North Burma there might be a dozen separate colonies.

What seems certain is that if it were possible to make a complete census of slipper-orchid colonies in North Burma every year for ten consecutive years, the figures and localities would vary widely from year to year. Of course this particular colony may have been a revival after years of rest. I had passed this way a number of times before; had it been visible I should surely have seen it. But it may have existed even earlier, before I first went there. Colonies come and go, no one knows why. Orchid seeds take a long time to produce a mature orchid plant—certainly many years.

The story of the life and death of the North Burma slipper orchid ought to end here, but surprisingly there is a sequel, which admirably illustrates the rise and fall of colonies.

Ever since my walk from the Yangtze to the Irrawaddy, when I first noticed *Paphiopedilum wardii*, I had kept a sharp eye open for slipper orchids, especially in the winter months when most of them flower (in cultivation under glass they prefer to flower after the new year). Two years after the disappearance of the original colony I went as botanist with an American expedition to the Hpimaw and Htawgaw hills on the North Burma–China frontier.

This was primarily a zoological expedition, organized and led by two friends of mine, Suydam Cutting and Arthur Vernay.

*Notched logs sometimes afford the only means of scaling a precipice
in the Tsangpo Gorge, Tibet*

The nutmeg scent of this
lovely rhododendron betrays
it from afar—Rhododendron
megacalyx in Tibet

Left:
A devout Tibetan has decorated
this prayer-carved slab on a
roadside mendong in Mönyul,
Assam, with the white flowers of
Rhododendron polyandrum

These lively Americans had sponsored and led many renowned expeditions to remote parts of the world on behalf of the American Museum of Natural History, and were never happier than when they were in the jungle. The expert zoologist of the team was Harold Anthony, on the staff of the same museum—a delightful companion with a vein of vinegar humour which was irresistible. In addition to the three Americans, Arthur and Suydam had invited two Englishmen to join them—J. K. Stanford, a great authority on the birds of Burma, and myself, who had some knowledge of the flora.

Stanford, known to his friends affectionately as J.K., was really the kingpin. He was the only member of the expedition who could speak Kachin, the principal language (not dialect) of North Burma. He knew the country and the people as well as the birds; and, having been a Deputy Commissioner in Burma, knew just how to organize an expedition. All problems of servants and transport were solved, and solved well, by J.K. Not only did he look after the day-to-day running of the expedition, but he hunted with the best, putting in an immense amount of work. His all-round knowledge and experience were invaluable.

So, while we owed a well-found expedition, with no stint in anything which might further our objects, to the generosity of the leaders and the driving force behind their personalities, it was to J.K. we owed the fact that everything ran smoothly, on silent silver wheels. The Hpimaw and Htawgaw hills is a corner of North Burma I had visited twice before. It was therefore comparatively familiar to me, though half a dozen visits would by no means exhaust its possibilities for the botanist. That had been some time ago. But such places do not change much; what does change is one's own knowledge and experience. As a result of increased experience, I noticed far more now than I had on my former journeys. Crossing the first range on our way north (J.K. and I had gone ahead to prepare camps), I suddenly caught sight of a fine slipper orchid with a glistening honey-yellow lip, and a purple standard edged with pure white. It was not, as one would naturally expect, growing in the ground; it was growing on the limb of a tree, like any epiphyte. In fact, this particular plant *was* an epiphyte.

I was hopping with delight, too excited to speak, though my heart was bursting with joy and pride. I had no idea what it was, except that it was a fine slipper orchid. It might be new, or it might not; anyway it was well worth collecting. I had no difficulty in climbing the tree and prising it off then and there. I showed my latest find with pride and glee to J.K., who had just returned to the rest-house. He too had scored a success, having collected a very rare bird, new to Burma if not to science. We sat down and exchanged stories, with a wealth of detail.

As J.K. would be returning this way shortly, to meet Arthur Vernay and Suydam Cutting, I asked him to speak to the rest-house *durwan* and promise him good money for every plant he could find. We showed him the specimens; he said he recognized them, and agreed to collect as many as I liked. It was common, he said, almost contemptuously. J.K. would take them back to Myitkyina with him, and post them to England without delay. Unfortunately, though the *durwan* said he would know the plant when he saw it again, he was either fatuously optimistic, or on the make. He obviously didn't know the plant at all. Neither did J.K., who was easily taken in. (Strange how, to the unprofessional eye, one plant or one bird can resemble another!) The result was, I paid good money for a parcel of plants sent to England, which, however rare and refreshing, were not what I wanted. But plants of the orchid I collected myself and sent to Maymyo Botanic Garden, in Burma, as an insurance, flourished.

The very next day I found it for the second time, growing on the road bank—a more orthodox habitat. It was not rare in the foothills at an altitude of four thousand feet or so. But a number of people, botanists and others, had been this way through the years since the bridle-path was made, most of them in the cold weather. (In the rainy season nobody travels in North Burma if they can help it.) Yet, so far as I knew, no one had ever mentioned a slipper orchid. It was just the kind of flower even the layman would speak about if he saw it; and so conspicuous was it in bloom that he couldn't miss it growing by the roadside. The most unbotanically minded person must have been struck by it, and made some attempt to preserve and perhaps to grow it. I began to wonder how many more species of slipper orchid grew in the Burmese jungle. Undoubtedly there was room for several more.

This plant proved to be *Paphiopedilum villosum*, first discovered near Moulmein many years ago, and later in the Shan States. Moulmein is about 750 miles south of Htawgaw, and a straight line between them passes through the Shan States at what is practically the half-way point. So there was nothing very remarkable in finding *P. villosum* near Htawgaw, though it was a considerable northward extension.

But what did surprise me was to find, a month or two later, a colony of *P. wardii* growing on another roadside bank at Htawgaw. It was not its presence there that was surprising, but the fact that it too had never been noticed before. Here it was, right beside the path, in full view of the passer-by; and in the many years since I had first known Htawgaw, half a dozen botanists and plant-collectors—myself included—had passed the spot. Why had none of us seen it?

But when I worked it out I knew the answer at once. No one had seen it because, generally speaking, before this winter it wasn't there. Obviously it was a new colony, flowering for the first time as the vigorous young plants proclaimed. They must of course have been there for a good many years before they flowered—but out of flower they could easily be overlooked. So I acquitted myself of lack of observation. The last time I was in Htawgaw (and that was twenty years earlier) the slipper orchid hadn't been there at all; or if it was it had certainly been too small to see. In any case, that was in the middle of the rainy season. I think that but for a stroke of luck *P. wardii* might easily be unknown in Europe to-day.

A summary of its botanical history could be interpreted something like this: by 1922 plants growing from wind-borne seeds were established on the Mali-Tisang divide. They must have been there for several years before that, perhaps as many as ten, because orchid-seeds take a long time to germinate and grow into recognizable plants, and still longer to reach flowering age. After another eight years a considerable colony had sprung up. There must have been many small, more or less unrecognizable plants coming on when I noticed the first flower. So the colony may have increased at a normal rate for about ten years, and reached its peak about 1931 when I saw it for the second time.

Then it began to decline, presumably still at the natural rate; after seven or eight years it was virtually extinct at the original site. But thirty miles distant a new colony had sprung up on a main bridle-path, though not yet of flowering age. Then three years later I found yet another small but flourishing colony, with plants in flower at Htawgaw a hundred miles away—measured straight across the mountains.

Can we draw any conclusions from these facts? Is the cycle of
existence for the species, or for the colony, constant? And what
limits the life of a plant? Is the soil exhausted, or the supply of
mycorrhiza used up? Or has the colony outstripped the growth
of mycorrhiza? The evidence does not so far divulge the answers.
I merely note that *P. wardii* was growing in one spot at the top
of the Tisang-Tamai divide for at least twenty years, assuming it
had been there for five years before I found it. For all I know, it
may be growing there again now.

The nearest relatives of this charming slipper orchid live in
Malaya and the Philippines; thus it is an outlier of its own little
group, and a link between the flora of North Burma and Malaya.
That is its claim to fame. For in spite of its striking colours and
neat shape, it gets low marks—or none—from the professional
orchid fanciers. In cultivation it flowers at about the same time
as in Burma, or rather later. And I recall, without pride, that it
took me just ten years to introduce it!

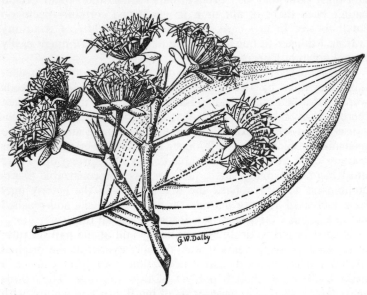

Rima Dogwood
(*Cornus chinensis*)

·11·

Glorious Dogwood

ON the afternoon of August 15, 1950, my wife and I were feeling at least contented, if not dynamically happy. The truth is, so little had happened for so long that we had lost all positive sensation of present happiness. Happiness became something to look forward to, not to experience now. But at last the future looked set fair, after four months of depression. One disappointment had followed another, and still we waited and hoped for the porters who were to carry our equipment, but who never came. And when in the sultry heat of an August afternoon they came unexpectedly, it hardly seemed to matter. We had grown almost indifferent. Even at the highest altitudes the primulas and rhododendrons we wanted so much to see were long since over. Never again would we set eyes on the sheaves and enormous tapestries of flowers in heavenly colours, which are a peculiar feature of these distant mountains.

Now autumn was in sight, and autumn colour can be glorious too. But not with flowers. Nevertheless we sat on the slab of rock at the look-out point near our camp that evening, as we had done a hundred times before, watching the river below us, in a sort of frenzy to read our fate in the waves, occasionally glancing aside at the path behind. And when the porters came into view, first one, then another, and another—and another—a long, straggling file winding through the pine forest, we watched them in incredulous silence. Perhaps a secret flame of hope flickered up in my heart for a moment, but it quickly died. I could not believe that our long vigil was over.

In April we had no worries. We were in good time for the rhododendrons, though we might have missed the magnolias at their best; possibly the cherries also, and a few other trees.

In May we thought without despair that we would still see the rhododendrons, though the lower forest species might be nearly over. But the shadow of defeat came nearer.

In June I consoled myself with the reflection that this was the best month for alpine rhododendrons, and that primulas and Meconopsis would be in flower.

By July I was seriously worried. I still said it didn't matter—there would certainly be a few flowers left over, enough perhaps to indicate at least, if indifferently, what they had looked like. We could fill in the blanks with a little imagination.

But by August we didn't care. Of course, in the high alps quite a lot of flowers hang on late, and we could get a good idea of the plants that had been. I have seen June-flowering alpine plants growing near, or under, patches of unmelted snow, still in bud in September. Anyway, we were in very good time for the harvest. Our spirits were down almost to zero, but we clung on—indeed, we had no choice. The march down the left bank (our side) of the Lohit River was extremely difficult—in fact, dangerous—and we still had to get our porters from Rima (Chayu). It would be far safer and more sensible, when (or if ever) we got porters, to go to Rima, cross the river there by rope bridge, and march down the right bank. But when unexpectedly the Rima men came to take us, not just back to the village, but to an alpine camp, our spirits did begin to revive a little.

The next day we returned to Rima across the cliff face, following a scarcely existent path which had always frightened me. Here, a month previously, a pony bringing us rice from Rima had slipped and fallen straight to its death in the raging river.

It was an exhausting march, trapped as we were between the rock cliffs on either side, which stored up the midday heat and let it ooze out slowly till long after dark. We camped close to the village, by the irrigation channel which took off water from the torrent higher up, where it emerged from the gorge.

The porters agreed to take us into the mountains two days' march. Rima itself is at five thousand feet. If we climbed three thousand feet a day we should finally camp at eleven thousand or twelve thousand feet. That meant near the timber line— trees, as opposed to scrub and bush—and there would be open meadow, moraines, cliffs, all the places where alpine plants grow. So late in the season was it that we might as well stay in the mountain camp till we finally left, about the end of October. It would mean the difference between success and failure. What had begun so badly, when we first reached Rima in the spring, seemed to be ending well. Much as we had missed, we should not have missed everything. The best flowers were over; but it was not so late that the plants would have died down and become lost in the universal dissolution; it should be easy to find and collect seed of almost everything. There would even be flowers in September—plenty of them, especially Saussurea and other Compositae, and Saxifrage; best of all, there would be gentians. So on that mid-August afternoon we felt tranquil. Our patience had not been in vain; we had never resigned ourselves to total failure.

I had no fear that the porters would let us down. True, we had been all set to start on August 14, but the headman had come and asked us to wait till the 16th, as his people had not quite finished their work in the fields. It was a reasonable request, and the two days' wait did not inconvenience us. One thinks these things over soberly in retrospect, and wonders at the strange causes which intervene to divert what seems the normal course of events. But then, *is* it the normal course of events? Why should we happen to be in the Lohit valley in the fateful year 1950 anyway? Whether it is normal or abnormal, seems to depend on where one breaks into the chain of causation.

Anyway, we could now say quite happily, To-morrow we start for the alps! By to-morrow evening we shall be collecting hardy plants, some of which we have never seen before!

I did say it, a dozen times.

During that short but glorious week in early April, when we were the guests of the Jongpen of exclusive Rima, we had not been idle. Rima, with its satellite villages, stands in an enclave in the eastern range immediately below the confluence of two rivers which unite to form the Lohit. (This range is the Brahmaputra–Irrawaddy divide.) The territory consists of two sloping, partly cultivated terraces situated one above the other, separated by an escarpment about six hundred feet high. One or two streams emerge from sword cuts in the mountains behind, and have entrenched themselves deeply in the loose material of the slope. We decided to explore one of these streams up to the point where it came out of its gorge.

Starting from the upper terrace, we ascended slowly towards the cliffs above, following the brink of the dry ravine. Various small trees and shrubs grew scattered on its crumbling slope, which I was surprised to find was too steep to descend. Our attention was quickly drawn to one small tree, and held there. It was leafless and in full bloom, and we stared at it in some amazement, unable at first to think what it could be. It grew on the almost vertical side of the ravine, but its crown came level with the terrace. I did not doubt we could easily stretch out an arm and pluck it. However, it turned out to be farther away than it looked, well out of reach; nor did the smooth trunk look climbable, even if I had been able to descend the cliff. Another tree ahead now came into view. But again we were foiled, and trees on the opposite side of the ravine were even more inaccessible. All this was very unsatisfactory, but there was every reason to suppose that sooner or later we would come across a tree we could reach.

What manner of tree was it?

From a short distance the leafless twigs are, in April, seen to be covered with spherical mop-heads of tiny sulphur-yellow flowers. Each twig or branchlet ends in a scarcely noticeable awl point of bronze-coloured, tightly twisted leaves—in short, a bud; and from immediately beneath them the mops, in pairs, spring from the axils of last year's leaf scars.

All this one could see through a good field-glass; but the details of the flower mops could not be made out till we got specimens. A well-grown tree thirty or forty feet tall will carry hundreds of glistening golden-flushed mop-heads, many of them in close clusters, the flowers of one being entangled with those of another. A more glorious sight in the early spring, out in the open parkland with dark pine-trees behind, can hardly be imagined.

Thus the Rima dogwood recalls *Cornus mas*, though it is a taller tree, with a smooth palm-like stem, and much larger mops composed of more flowers, of a luminous sulphur-yellow instead of gloomy orange; a graceful, airy thing to herald the annual rebirth of the forest. For whereas the flowers of *Cornus mas* are often dim and glum, almost one might say dull, the fluffy yellow flowers of the Rima dogwood diffuse a delightful effect of brilliant sunshine. What a glorious sight an avenue of it in full bloom would be. We decided to give all the time necessary to finding more specimens. Fruit we must get, whatever the cost.

However, this day we had to return to camp empty-handed so

far as the Cornus was concerned. We saw half a dozen specimens, but not one of them was accessible. Possibly some of the villagers could help, and if all else failed we might be able to hack down a tree in fruit. But that was vandalism, only to be indulged in as a last resort.

A few days later our excellent cook, Phag Tsering, a tough, undersized, but well-proportioned little Nepali, asked for a day off to go plant-hunting with a village friend. He did this occasionally, and as he almost invariably brought back something good, we were only too glad to encourage him. He had been trained by no less a plant-hunter than Frank Ludlow, chiefly in the Bhutan Himalaya, and in his dual rôle of cook and plant-hunter he did Ludlow credit.

Phag Tsering returned in the afternoon with several large branches of our Cornus in full bloom, and now for the first time I was able to examine the flowers at close quarters. It was a beautiful little tree, for though the separate flowers are small, as in all dogwoods (the splendid show put out by the American trees is of course due purely to their great up-curving bracts) the heads are large, with up to a hundred blossoms in each; on their silky extended diverging pedicels the individual flowers look like tiny shooting-stars.

The original genus Cornus has been severely but justifiably manhandled by American, British, Japanese, and Russian botanists during the last forty or so years, and its species are now allocated to five genera.[1] Cornus itself now includes only four species typified by *Cornus mas* (*Macrocarpium mas*); three splinter groups account for most of the familiar garden plants formerly known as species of Cornus. Thus *Cornus alba* and *Cornus sanguinea*, noteworthy for the bright red of its shoots in winter, are now *Thelycrania alba* and *Thelycrania sanguinea*; *C. stolonifera* has become *Th. sericea*; even little *Cornus canadensis*, which has been known under that name for generations, although admittedly very different in habit from the true dogwoods, has become *Chamaepericlymenum canadense*; lovely

[1] Those who want to pursue this matter of classification further will find it discussed by J. Hutchinson, in *Annals of Botany* (New Series) Vol. 6, pp. 83–93 (1942), H. Hara, in *Journal of Arnold Arboretum*, Vol. 29, pp. 111–115 (1948), A. I. Pojarkova, in *Notulae Syst. Herb. Inst. Bot. Komarov*, Vol. 12, pp. 164–180 (1950), and J. E. Dandy, in *Watsonia*, Vol. 4, pp. 46–47 (1957).

Cornus florida and *Cornus nuttallii* have changed to *Benthamidia florida* and *Benthamidia nuttallii*. This alteration of names has little to do with playful research into forgotten history, as horticultural cynics might suppose. The splitting of the unlikely and unwieldy, far too comprehensive genus Cornus, which had survived for too long as a ragbag for any bits or pieces, is justified by well-founded differences in the inflorescence and habit. Fortunately, it remains correct to call the Rima dogwood by the name under which I first knew the species, *Cornus chinensis*, and to treat the alternative name, *Macrocarpium chinense*, as a synonym.

The four small silky bracts, which form a sort of collar underneath each flower-head, are like bud-scales, quite unshowy, and turned right back out of the way, as though to display the crowded flowers to the best advantage.

The question was: Would it be hardy in Britain? We had absolutely no means of judging. All we knew for certain was that it grew at six thousand to seven thousand feet and could stand up to modest, if prolonged, frost. But Rima enjoys a hot, damp, though rather rainless, summer, which might make it vulnerable to phases of our unpredictable weather.[1]

We questioned Phag Tsering closely. Yes, he could find his way back to the tree when the time came for collecting the fruit. He saw only one specimen, but there might be more. . . . I put the deadline at the end of September or early October.

A fortnight later, from our camp by the Di Chu just inside the Indian frontier, we went up the gorge and camped for a couple of days in the forest, where rhododendrons, cherries, and silver-fir grew within reach of the spray. Here we found Cornus saplings, too young to flower, but in full leaf. The leaves were remarkably large for a Cornus, deep green and heavily veined, with long drip-tip.

It was after this little journey that our long wait began. For seventeen weeks we were immobilized in the dry Lohit valley ten miles below Rima. To our surprise and dismay our friend the Jongpen had informed us that we must not return to his village. Though we did not know it at the time, the Chinese invasion of Tibet was imminent, and the whole situation tricky

---

[1] Its behaviour in cultivation, so far, suggests that it would be hardy in the west generally, especially in Ireland. It might even be hardy in sheltered districts inland, in most years.

and confused—or possibly it was the Jongpen who was tricky and the situation confused. In any case, when, in August, the porters turned up so unexpectedly to welcome us back, it was not because the Jongpen had changed his mind but because he had changed his residence. He was no longer in Rima.

Neither the porters nor we could possibly know that by taking us away from the Di Chu camp they were saving our lives, any more than that by postponing the start from Rima for two days, they were to save them a second time.

We were tired that evening and ate our supper early. The day was hot and dry as usual. The strong up-valley wind, which had blown for hours, was dying down, and a surf of shapeless cloud hid the tops of the high hills. One cannot see far into the distance from Rima, so deeply is it sunk among the ranges; and all three valleys bend sharply here, throwing out great spurs which block the middle distance.

My wife turned in early, and was half asleep by twilight. For an hour I sat in the tent writing my diary. The hurricane lamp burned brightly, and I sat on, thinking of the next day's climb. Where would we be sleeping the following night, I wondered?

There came a sudden, swift jolt, but nothing moved inside the tent. My wife woke and sat up. "What was that?" she asked sleepily. A few seconds later there came a sustained noise from outside, like distant thunder, not alarming in any way, though I wondered what it was if not thunder. It ceased suddenly, and I went to the entrance, curious to know just what was happening. I felt no qualms. Why indeed should I? Drawing aside the flaps of the tent, I looked out at the calm sky. The stars were shining, though it was not yet full dark, and I leant against the stout metal pole to enjoy the beauty of the night and feel the cool mountain air on my cheek.

The tent faced north, and I could just see the great ridge two or three miles away, which shut out the view up the two divergent valleys. My eyesight's gone funny, I thought. I really must do something about it. For the trees along the skyline, which one could see distinctly on a clear day, looked fuzzy; no doubt it was a trick of the dusk, but they certainly appeared to be dancing up and down, very fast. I suppose it was a matter of a few seconds only before the wave of seismic movement reached us.

I turned to my wife. "What's happening?" I asked. But she

had already leapt out of bed. The truth dawned on us simultaneously.

"Earthquake! " we shouted to each other, in a surprised tone of voice.

"Outside, quick! " I said, as though the big tent were a stone tower about to topple down on our heads. And indeed I did fear lest we be entangled among ropes and billowing canvas. But more than anything, I was afraid of fire. I seized the hurricane lamp from the table and set it down outside. It toppled over and went out immediately.

We were now in darkness; not absolute darkness, but we could see little of our surroundings in the deep summer dusk.

"Lie down flat," I said; and at that very moment we were thrown flat on the stony, dry sand close beside the tent.

A terrific noise now assailed our ears, compounded of many noises, none of which sounded familiar. It was a dull uproar, without the purposeful emphasis of thunder, though it was amorphous as thunder. My wife and I lay side by side holding hands while the ground hammered against our bodies with the rapidity of a kettledrum roll. The whole earth trembled. There was a light in the servants' tent, and I could see shadows moving on the canvas.

"Come out," we yelled to them, but we might as well have shouted against the noise of a storm at sea. However, the two boys tumbled out of the tent, tripping over the guy ropes in their fearful haste, and flung themselves down, or perhaps were thrown down, close to us. Stretching out my left arm, I found Phag Tsering's right hand and gripped it tight. He was calling out incoherent prayers. Akkey also was praying aloud. The four of us were now all in touch, holding hands and ready to help each other.

How long the drumming beneath us, above us, all round us, continued I don't know. Three or four minutes certainly, perhaps longer; it seemed ageless.

My wife and I talked a little, calmly. I felt we had only a few minutes to live, that the end was very near, and all must be said now. I was not conscious of fear; on the contrary, I felt curiously elated. How the end would come I did not know, but I expected the crust all round us to break up suddenly like thin ice when too great a weight is put upon it. Then we would go straight through. But somehow I felt certain the end would be swift and merciful, that we should suffer neither pain nor terror. I did not believe that we might have to struggle for our lives; had I done so, I must have been afraid. Stark paralysing fear came much later, and was only indirectly due to the earthquake —the old fear of heights which has always turned my insides to water.

Afterwards I wondered why I had been so insistent that we lie flat on the ground. Was it instinct, to distribute our weight over as large an area as possible, lest we break through the thin floor into the boiling cauldron beneath? Partly that, I think, but partly the instinct to cling to mother earth as firmly as possible, even at her most terrifying.

I expected the ground to heave and roll. It did not; it only drummed. Presently the pandemonium all round us changed key. There was only one noise now, and that unmistakable—the noise of big rocks falling in heavy showers, sliding, grinding, bouncing all round us. But the valley was full of terrible echoes. A little way up the slope from our camp was the high escarpment which separated the upper and lower terraces. If that gave way we should be overwhelmed, buried without trace. Even if there was no general collapse, a boulder as large, perhaps, as a taxicab might be shot like a mighty projectile out of the cliff and come singing through the air; anything that got in its way would be smashed like an egg. Luckily for us, this cliff, though built partly of loose material, survived.

For some little time longer we lay on the ground. I felt strangely reluctant to get up. Before I did so a most curious thing happened.

The continuous din and roar of falling rocks had now become intermittent, and we could talk more comfortably. Suddenly, without the slightest warning or explanation, came very loud and clear a single explosion, like an instantaneous crack of thunder. The noise seemed to come from the north-west, and from up in the air, though not far away. It was followed a few seconds later by a second explosion exactly like the first, neither louder nor less loud; and that after a similar interval by a third and a fourth, all exactly alike, at exact intervals, up to a sixth. Then silence. The explosions were smooth and sharp, without echoes or rough edges, and sounded exactly like a stick of Ack-Ack shells bursting round a plane. In the ensuing silence the next rock avalanche sounded ragged.

We got up slowly and went inside the tent, from which we had emerged so precipitately perhaps half an hour before. Nothing had changed. The clock was ticking regularly on the table beside a mug of water. Everything was in its place. For a moment I thought that we would be leaving for our alpine camp the next morning, and that I must finish packing; there had been a momentary interruption. . . .

And yet, in the words of the novelist, our world lay broken around us, as I quickly realized when I went outside again. Not a star showed, although half an hour before the ribbon of sky overhead had been bright with the splendid northern constellations. I was not yet aware of the thick curtain of dust which had spread across the valley from the mountains around us. But already our throats were dry, and we decided we must all drink tea. We felt we needed it.

Just then there came an anguished cry from Phag Tsering— "Water! Water! "

That was alarming. Was he at the point of death, crying out for water? Had the Lohit, dammed below, risen fifty feet in no time at all, and was the flood about to engulf us? Or was the big stream from the upper terrace, where the dogwood grew, out of control and sweeping down upon the camp?

We dashed across to Phag Tsering's side, and were in time to see our ample water supply, which, drawn off a torrent, ran along a channel to the cultivated slope to irrigate the paddy-fields, shrinking quickly to a trickle. The flume was dammed.

Seizing every utensil we could lay hands on, we strove desperately to fill them before the trickle dried up completely. Buckets, basins, saucepans, even mugs, were pressed into service; but we had scarcely filled them before the water suddenly ceased to flow.

The remaining hours of darkness were unforgettable. We could see little in the darkness through the increasing dust cloud; but the faint outlines of the ranges were still there, and we could hear the river. The trembling world, in the throes of settling down, heaved and groaned at short intervals, and with each spasm roared like an express train emerging from a tunnel. I slept for an hour or two, but appear to have been the only person in camp who did.

And what of the village itself? How had it fared in all this turmoil? At dawn I got up and went out to look at the country.

A pall of dust hung in the sky, and behind it the invisible sun rose in a red smear.

The farther landscape was not so very different from what it had been twenty-four hours ago, except that the dark slopes in every direction were striped with broad white scars and gashes. Here and there mountain summits had broken away, and the crests of spurs been sheered off; however, the hard grim lines of the hills had not softened. But when I looked closely at the immediate foreground the damage was plain enough. Every house in the village had lost its roof, and the little monastery lay on its side in ruins. More to the point, I observed that the bamboo rope bridge across the river had snapped like a thread. Until that was replaced we could not return to India direct.

But there is no need to say anything more about one of the greatest earthquakes ever recorded, whose birth pang was within twenty-five miles of Rima. Only the part it played in the story of the dogwood is relevant.

We could now count our blessings. It had been a near thing for us. We had been saved from an unpleasant death when we left the Di Chu camp on August 10, for, as we discovered later, the spot had been swept by a perfect avalanche of large boulders. Again, had we started up the mountain for Rima on the day originally intended, we must have been killed by rock-falls in our camp; or, had we survived the first onslaught, while trying to make our way out of the trap. The destruction up the gorge we had intended to follow was appalling. Or had the earthquake came a day or two later, we must have been caught high up. We were in no doubt as to our immediate problems. Two things remained: to collect seed of the dogwood, and to get out of Rima. We must also find clean water.

Morning after morning the sun rose into a fog behind the ranges. During the next fortnight I hunted diligently for the dogwood without success. The few trees we had discovered in April could still not be reached; I searched for others, but found none. The damage on the slope up which Phag Tsering had climbed to find his tree was considerable, and it seemed very doubtful whether he would be able to reach it. He himself was in no doubt on the point; he would not even make the attempt.

"Get hold of the man who accompanied you when you found it. I will go with him," I said. "He must show me the way and we'll try to reach the tree."

But I was worried. Would the fruits be ripe? It was now early September; was it worth while collecting them at all? On the other hand, we must get out of Rima as soon as we could, for the best of reasons: we, and the village too, were short of food, and were drinking stagnant water from the paddy-fields. If we couldn't get across the river we would *have* to stay where we were; but I dared not risk holding on till the second or third week in September, even for the sake of the dogwood, if the way was open. I tried the way north up the left bank of the Lohit, and got a mile or two before being stopped completely by rock falls. There seemed to be no immediate prospect of leaving. So far all attempts by the villagers, with the assistance of people living on the other side, had failed to get a line across the swollen river, though they had tried at several different places. Until the flood went down we were marooned. That might not be till October or November.

Meanwhile the after-effects of the earthquake continued, and subterranean noises, followed by tremors, often severe, were of hourly occurrence. They went on by day and by night, and continued, though at gradually increasing intervals and decreasing strength, for months. Avalanches of rocks poured down the shattered cliffs, and these demonstrations were the most frightening of all. In places falls occurred so regularly that you could have set your watch by them—a most peculiar phenomenon.

Millions of tons of stuff rolled into the river. Whole forests slid down. The dust hung in a venomous cloud over the broken mountains. Though the tearing midday wind tried hard to break through and roll it up, it never succeeded. Dust lay like a thick grey powder on every leaf of every plant that survived. The wholesale destruction of vegetation was terrible to see. Occasionally the sun showed through the dust cloud for an hour or two, looking like a burnished copper gong; but more often it was hidden, and dust was in our eyes and throats, and gritting on our skins. Always it was in our food.

On the twentieth day after the earthquake we heard that the rope bridge had been repaired. Now I had to act quickly. In two or three days the porters would be ready, and we could start for India. I must not put off the dogwood another day. And suppose that after all we couldn't reach the tree? Well, it would be just too bad, and there was nothing I could do about it. All my trips to the upper terrace, which had been roughly treated by the

*Lilium nepalense concolor—
a perfect specimen growing
in the Himalayan foothills*

*A very different lily from
Manipur—Lilium mackliniae*

Surely that's a new gentian on that cliff!
Plant-hunting on Sirhoi Kashong, Manipur

*Tight clusters of Gentiana
amoena, with sky-blue flowers,
form vivid patches of colour
among high-alpine shrubs*

Below: *Gentiana gilvostriata opens its dazzling cobalt-blue flowers in autumn, after
the rains, in North Burma*

*Paphiopedalum wardii (Cypri-
pedium wardianum), a graceful
slipper orchid with flowers
chocolate and green, discovered
by the author in North Burma.
It grows on rocks and banks
in the evergreen rain forest
at 5000 ft. altitude*

earthquake, had ended in failure. I must get hold of the guide at once, and visit Phag Tsering's dogwood without delay.

But after all I did not have to go, as it turned out. Late that afternoon Phag Tsering and a friend arrived in camp with an armful of dogwood branches covered with berries. Apparently the climb was not quite so desperate as he had supposed; but he made the most of his story. I was sincerely grateful to him.

Few of the berries were black and soft, denoting ripeness, but several of the red ones gradually turned darker, and some days later seemed to be more or less ripe.

The few seeds secured on this expedition, after a hazardous two months' journey in our keeping, through the Lohit Gorge and on across the plains of Assam, eventually reached England safely. The majority were not sufficiently ripe to stand the chances and changes of prolonged transportation; but the Royal Horticultural Society raised half a dozen plants, which grew strongly. Three were put out to grass in the Wisley garden and survived three or four winters on Battleston Hill, only to perish in the disastrous arctic wave of January and February 1956.

However, one of the half-dozen original plants, kept under glass, and planted in a large tub, survived, and happily Mr Frank Hanger, the Curator of Wisley Gardens, has had some success with cuttings. He has increased the tenuous stock and some of these have already been distributed.

Should I live to see this dogwood flower in England,[1] I shall inevitably think of it as a tree which is not only beautiful, but which has a tale of miraculous escape attached to it. My one regret is that it cannot be re-christened *terratremula*.

But one does rather wonder why this beautiful tree, which is recorded sparingly from Yunnan, Szechwan, Kweichow, and Kwangtung, as well as from North Burma, Assam, and southeast Tibet, was not introduced to Europe half a century ago. There can be no doubt that the Rima form of it, at its most westerly known station, is by far the finest.

[1] Kingdon Ward never lived to see it in flower in England as he hoped, but a flowering specimen grown at Windsor Great Park was exhibited before the Royal Horticultural Society in March 1960. This specimen has reached the 20-foot high roof of a glasshouse, producing flower-clusters 1 inch across early in the year, followed by leaves up to 1 foot long and 5½ inches wide.—W. T. S.

·12·

Coffin-trees

THE English, naturally enough, are concerned about the ever-rising cost of living. The Chinese, especially the rich Chinese, must be equally concerned about the ever-rising cost of dying. In China good burial is more important than good birth. The most vital thing in life is to be buried well. The surest sign of good burial is a grand funeral; and the symbol of a grand funeral is a grand coffin. The Chinese have a saying: The best thing to look forward to in life is a good funeral.

Sooner or later every one needs a coffin, so the sooner you have one the better. Why put off till to-morrow what might be wanted to-day? No doubt that is why, to a Chinaman, a coffin is a useful piece of household furniture, which he buys (if he can afford it) when he sets up house on his own, surrounded by his needy relations. The coffin may be stacked in a corner, out of the way, being for the time more ornamental than functional; but that is no disparagement. Can he buy it on the instalment system? If not, he can at least buy it on a mortgage.

A coffin should last at least two or three years, at the end of which time the corpse is finally buried. Then, if all goes well, the outer man is cast off, as the covering of a chrysalis is cast off before it becomes a butterfly. Even in sleep the butterfly spirit withdraws temporarily from the body, to hover near by, but returns just as the sleeper wakes; that is why it is unwise to awaken a man suddenly from sleep, lest his spirit be taken by surprise and has not time to slip back unobserved into its chrysalis before some mishap befall it. The dead Chinaman must enter the spirit world intact, with his skeleton complete. And here the chrysalis is as important as the butterfly itself—as he leaves this world, so he arrives in the next; no repairs are done in the spirit world. To arrive legless means a continuance of leglessness throughout eternity; hence the importance of a sound coffin, and a three-year plan.

The countless millions of poor in China can only afford the cheapest of coffins (if any), and a shallow grave outside the city wall. These cheap coffins, made of some shoddy wood, quickly rot to pieces, and before long the starving dogs, jackals, wolves, or vultures disinter and dismember the corpses. This is very humiliating for the corpse, and hardly less so for his relations and ancestors. Thus the future is bleak for the vast majority of Chinese. The *élite* survive death decently; the poor usually depart this life more maimed than they entered it. The only thing which can ensure a happy ending to the most blameless life in China is a really good coffin.

Compared to the very large number of tree species native to China, those from which first-class coffins can be made are few. Forests, like other natural resources (and not in China only), are a dwindling asset; and coffin-trees disappear faster than most. Hence the ever-rising cost.

The best coffin-trees are conifers such as Libocedrus, Cunninghamia, and Taiwania, the latter a comparative newcomer. The resinous wood is durable under all conditions; and this is the quality which has top priority. A few hardwoods—that is, broad-leafed trees—are also long-lasting, especially the famous 'scented-wood-tree' Machilus, a laurel found in tropical China. With the charmingly child-like vagueness of Chinese nomenclature, this is called *nan shu*. It means "tree of the south." *Nan shu* is related to an even more famous Chinese (though not exclusively Chinese) laurel, the camphor tree, Cinnamomum. Both trees have aromatic wood, though the camphor of commerce is distilled from the leaves.

The resin of softwoods, or the essential oils of certain hardwoods, are of course highly prized as preservatives. There are perhaps a dozen species of tree known to the Chinese which are in the top class for coffins. The coffins themselves are of such good workmanship, and of such solid construction, that no harm is likely to come to them, or to the occupant; especially as they may never be put into the ground at all.

Probably there are other laurels which would serve almost as well as *nan shu*, although I do not know of any others so used. But considering the shortages, it is possible that people are having a look round for substitutes. They would do well to remember that the sub-tropical (or warm-temperate) broad-leafed forest belt of South-east Asia is largely a laurel belt, where these beautiful evergreen-trees occur in great variety. The trouble is that not all of them grow big enough to produce suitable coffin-planks. Size of tree is a limiting factor. The Englishman is conscious of his social importance when he lives in a large house, drives a large car, and is surrounded by large gardens, but the Chinaman only feels conscious of his importance when he is surrounded by a large coffin, a coffin as large as life.

The mandarin's coffin is a very impressive piece of furniture. It has the traditional coffin shape, only more so, and is built up of six pieces of timber well joined together—two side-pieces, two small but immensely thick end-pieces, a floor-piece, and a huge lid. The lid is about nine feet long, three feet wide at the rounded head, tapering to two feet, and perhaps three inches thick. The base and two side-pieces are shorter and narrower. The end-pieces are roughly square and much thicker, especially in the middle where they slope up to a central boss; but of course they are far smaller than the four long planks. Base and lid overlap at the ends, and to a lesser extent at the sides; especially the lid, which is the kingpin of the whole coffin. The end-pieces are usually carved. The weight of such a coffin is in the neighbourhood of four hundred or five hundred pounds, and that before the lacquer, black or scarlet, is laid on thick. It needs eight or ten coolies to carry it; the more coolies, the finer the funeral.

The frantic urge to find good coffin-trees for their wealthy citizens is perhaps the driving force which has caused the Chinese to overrun almost every tropical land in South-east Asia where, if they do not actually outnumber the native population, they form self-contained communities. They are more hard-working than the natives, and presently control the economy, as, for instance, in Siam and Malaya.

The greatest problem with regard to new coffin-trees discovered in the mountains of far west China is, of course, the problem of getting the wood out. Vast as are (or were) the forests of China, they could not last for ever without conservation. But the Chinese lived in a static world. For them nothing changed; and when the coffin-trees virtually disappeared from accessible places they were astonished. They had to find new coffin-trees. But the only likely places, at least in China itself, were in the far west, and transport difficulties were formidable. The weight of a

single coffin plank in the raw may be as much as 130 pounds,
and eighty or ninety pounds is common.

Many years ago, while I was waiting in Hongkong for a ship to
Borneo, I took the daily ferry-boat to Canton. During the two
days I spent on Shameen island, one of the places I visited was
a temple in the city known as the Temple of the Dead.

I was taken through an ornate gateway, across a paved
courtyard, up some steps, and into a pavilion; then across a
second courtyard and into the temple itself. The darkness was
illuminated only by a few candles, which threw grotesque
shadows of coffins on walls and ceiling. For the hall was filled
with coffins along the walls; and down the centre; in places
they were two or three deep, piled one on top of the other.
And what coffins! They were of the largest size and richest
decoration, heavily lacquered in black and sealing-wax red,
with gold scrolling. Some of them must have cost a fortune—
hundreds of Haikwan taels. All contained dead Chinese of
high rank, or perhaps rich merchants, awaiting final burial.

It was a sound principle of the old imperial administration that
an official could not serve in his own province. Thus viceroys,
governors, taotais, and others of high estate who administered
justice in Canton might have come from anywhere except Canton;
from as far away as Kansu or from as near at hand as Kwangsi.
But though a Chinese governor could not serve in his own province, he could not be buried anywhere but in his own city or
village. Thus it often, and perhaps usually, happened that when
he died his family, having put him in his costly coffin, had not
the money to pay for its transport, by land and river, across a
thousand or fifteen hundred miles of rough country—a journey
which would take several weeks, or even months. They therefore
stored the corpse, in its coffin, in this crypt in Canton, while they
tried to save up the money for the last journey home. It must not
be supposed that they grudged this service to their relations.
Filial piety in China is strong, and the priests of the temple were
paid, not only for housing the coffins, but for supplying small
cups of tea and other light refreshments to the dead! Nor was
the cost of the journey the only source of delay. A Chinese must
be buried on "the auspicious day," determined by astrologers;
and this might not occur for months or even years.

Some of the coffins I saw in Canton had been there for many

months. Thus the importance of a good strong coffin, which would protect the dead man on his long rough journey, becomes clear.

I was once lucky enough to find a coffin-tree, and to see this industrial machine at work. In 1906 a Japanese botanist found an unknown conifer in Formosa. He sent specimens to Tokyo University, and the new plant was described and named by Professor Takeda. He called it *Taiwania cryptomerioides*, which might be translated "the conifer from Taiwan, which is something like a cryptomeria." A few years later it was found in North Burma by a forest officer addicted to botany, J. H. Lace; but no connexion with the Formosan tree was suggested for many years. It is the exception for Indian Forest officers to collect plants, or indeed to know any field botany at all; and Lace's herbarium specimens went into the archives and didn't come out again for twenty years.

But the Chinese who live in Yunnan, just over the mountains from where this Taiwania was found, had long known of the tree. They were probably working it years before either the Japanese collector, or Lace, discovered it. And about 1912, when rumours of its existence in large numbers along the Burma–China frontier became rife, there was already a brisk export trade from the Htawgaw and Hpimaw hills. The trade centred round the little Lisu village of Kangfang, on the upper Ngawchaung River; and some years later I visited Kangfang while botanizing at Hpimaw, a long day's march away. In those days the coffin-plank industry was organized from the city of Tengueh, formerly called Momien and now called Tengchung.[1] Every cold weather the carpenters' guild sent trained craftsmen across the passes to fell trees, cut them up on the spot, saw them into planks, and shape them to their special purpose. It was skilled work which could not be left to the crude methods and cruder tools of the local hill tribes.

At the time of my first visit there were still trees standing at no great distance from Kangfang, though not in its immediate neighbourhood. The planks, already roughed out, were brought in and stood up to season for a year before the next step. Thus, though it was impossible to extract the trees themselves, it was possible to extract planks. The ruthless exploitation that followed, however, made even that difficult. Years later, when I next visited Kangfang, the industry was beginning to die out. I saw young

[1] Tengchwan.

trees which had been planted in Lisu villages, but no big trees grew anywhere near, though planks were still arriving from the north. They were being floated down the Ngawchaung River, which is low in winter. When I first visited the district, I had travelled on foot northward over the Wulaw Pass, and thence up the Nmai Hka, a difficult journey in the rainy season. Beyond the Wulaw I had passed through forests of Taiwania; and the distinguished Austrian botanist Heinrich Handel-Mazzetti, when in Yunnan, had collected seed from the trees still farther north. But under the conditions prevailing, without so much as a bridle-path, it would be impossible to extract even planks from such steep and distant country. So common is Taiwania in the forests which clothe the Burma–China frontier, I suspect it was formerly abundant at least as far south as Htawgaw; also, that the Chinese knew all about it long before it was found in Formosa. Unfortunately, it has now virtually disappeared from these comparatively accessible regions.

The trees belong to local villages, or even to individuals, and are bought by the Chinese. In those days a fully grown tree two hundred feet high might be worth a hundred rupees or more. If it yielded planks for a dozen coffins, which when finished might fetch six or seven hundred rupees each, there would still be a pretty profit, even allowing for the wages of all the carpenters, carriers, and others employed.

On my last visit to Kangfang I watched planks being floated down the turbulent but shallow Ngawchaung River, one man to every four planks, lashed together to make a raft. They were landed below Kangfang and carried up to the village on mules. Sometimes they were carried by mules all the way to China, one heavy plank laid flat on the pack-saddle along the animal's back, or two lighter planks lashed one on each side. But the heaviest planks were carried over the ten-thousand-foot Hpimaw Pass by Lisu coolies—a tremendous feat of human strength and endurance.

It was some time before I could persuade anyone to show me a full-grown tree. The interested Chinese were suspicious of my motives for wishing to see one. It would have required a long tough journey to reach the Wulaw Pass, and see again the pure stands I had seen many years before; while to search for the odd tree in the steep forests between Kangfang and Htawgaw would have taken many days, and might still have ended in failure.

Then a Maru who owned one tree which he had found near

Htawgaw promised to show it to me. We left Htawgaw in the afternoon and descended three thousand feet to the Ngawchaung River, which here flows through a gorge. Crossing the river by a cane suspension bridge, we ascended the mountain-side to a small village where we spent the night. An early start next morning was necessary if we were to get back to Htawgaw the same day, so after a quick breakfast we were on our way. It was a long steep climb by a rough and narrow track, at first through high grass, later in pine forest. Finally we reached the crest of a ridge; the going among the rocks was worse, but the slope eased off a little. On one side of us was a deep, steep-sided ravine filled with forest, mainly broad-leafed. For some time we continued to ascend, until we found rocks covered with the beautiful pink-flushed fragrant flowers of *Rhododendron bullatum*. We had now climbed more than three thousand feet, and I felt we must be nearing the coffin-tree. But the guide still went on. Suddenly he stopped. There were thick bushes on the edge of the ravine, hiding the forest. For a moment he hesitated.

"Are we there?" I asked, looking round doubtfully at the big rocks over which sprawled masses of rhododendron. The air was thick with their nutmeg scent.

The guide wagged his head. "It's near here, *duwa*."

He began to hack his way through the bushes. Presently he beckoned to me, peering and pointing. The forest, on the steep sheltered slope, was dense, in contrast to the open pine forest on the ridge. At first I could distinguish nothing but broad-leafed evergreen forest. It was obvious, however, that there were many different species. Following the direction with my eyes, I presently observed some little way down a pillar of reddish wood, straight as a dart, though the base was hidden from view by smaller trees. It seemed to disappear through the canopy and be lost to sight, like the magic beanstalk of the fairy-tale.

"The coffin-tree, *duwa*."

I nodded. "Let's go down to it," I said quietly. Actually I was almost speechless with excitement.

The side of the ravine was precipitous here, but we stamped a trail in the soft leafy earth, traversing down; and, cutting our way as we went, soon reached the base of the tree a hundred feet or more below. Meanwhile another man was hacking down the bushes which impeded the view from above.

I reckoned the Taiwania to be two hundred feet high and

fifty feet to the first branch. It towered up above the oaks, laurels, and other trees, like a cathedral spire above the roofs of the city; it might be two or three centuries old. The bark was soft and stringy, something like that of the Californian redwoods. It hung from the trunk in strips and tatters. For some time I stayed by the tree, measuring and feasting my eyes on it. I had brought my stand camera with me, and from above I was presently able to take two photographs; one of the trunk, and one of the pyramidal spire. It was impossible to get the whole tree into one picture.

It was a wonderful experience to have enjoyed such a view of a solitary coffin-tree, worth, so the owner told me, at least two hundred rupees. However, he had no intention of selling it at present—he reckoned it was only two hundred years old and would grow larger yet. Moreover, it would be rather difficult to extract. So we returned to the river and reached Htawgaw the same evening.

I have mentioned a hundred rupees as an average price for a mature tree. But that was before the war. It might well be double or treble that now. On the other hand, in those early days when Europeans were becoming acquainted with the tree it was relatively accessible. Now it is no longer so. The cost of extraction to-day must be immense, and the price of a tree in those remote forests may therefore be little more than it was. It may even be less.

Unless something is done soon to save the remaining trees, and re-planting schemes are set on foot, *Taiwania cryptomerioides* is likely to become locally extinct. If, on the other hand, communications up the eastern Irrawaddy are improved so much that trees at present inaccessible become easy to get at, the species may become finally extinct in Burma.

The Chinese discovery of the now famous *Metasequoia glyptostroboides* adds another possible coffin-tree to the short list. With willing Chinese co-operation, immediate steps were taken in the west to grow this lovely tree in Europe and in North America, where it is now well-established. One of the largest trees is in the Copenhagen Botanic Garden; it is about twenty-five feet high. Have the Chinese themselves taken any steps to cultivate it on a big scale? It would be ironic if, about the year 2200, Europe and America were exporting coffin-planks to China!

·13·

In search of Tea

IT is a truism to say that plants furnish not only a high proportion of the food of nearly all mankind, but nearly all the food of the greater part of mankind. Plants also supply man with many pleasant luxuries now regarded almost as necessities. One of these is tea. From time to time I have been obliquely associated with the tea industry, and it is of plant-hunting in this connexion that I write here.

Plants for food and medicinal plants are so important that most of those used to-day have been known for untold centuries. It is their cultivation on a commercial scale, and their world-wide consumption, that is comparatively modern. From the earliest times men have sought and used them. They have played an essential part in the evolution of civilization.

In India there are two well-equipped tea research stations, staffed by experts in every branch of science which has any bearing on the cultivation and manufacture of tea—that is to say, botanists, chemists, entomologists, mycologists, plant-pathologists, and others. A third research station takes care of tea in Ceylon. It is thanks to the skill of these experts, working with, and advising, tea-planters, that we have not only a sufficient world supply of tea, but ever-better-quality teas, at what in this country are called popular prices. Tea is, oddly enough, a camellia, and selected varieties of *Camellia sinensis*—the cultivated tea-plant—will, under the best conditions, yield almost one thousand pounds of finished tea per planted acre per annum.

So far as is known, all tea to-day is cultivated, or has at one time been cultivated. Neither Assam tea nor China tea has so far been found growing wild. The so-called 'wild tea' of Assam is only cultivated tea run wild after early village plantations have long been abandoned. But from time to time the Indian

Tea Association, at the request of Dr W. Wight, botanist at the Tocklai Experimental Station in Assam, has commissioned me to search for tea-like camellias. It was to be my business to collect material, including seeds, of any camellia found, and to report on its occurrence, and on its local use, if any.

I reviewed all the available evidence of the history of tea and its travels, and narrowed down the field in which it might be expected to grow wild. In the end I reached the conclusion that if wild tea existed at all it would be most likely to occur in the jungle-covered mountains between Assam and North Burma, a part of the world totally unexplored, at least botanically. In that remote region there exists a special attraction to the plant-hunter and geographical botanist—namely, an isolated mountain fifteen thousand feet high which has never been reached. The peak is called Dapha Bum. Moreover, the Mishmi hills region has a reputation for queer plants found nowhere else in India or outside it. Why that should be so no one knows. Perhaps it is indirectly connected with the fact that it is a violent country, where earthquakes, storms, and floods happen rather frequently and very suddenly.

And if wild tea were discovered, what then? Even if our tea is a hybrid plant it yields good tea. Would a variety straight out of the jungle be half as good? In any case, our tea-blenders never sell us the pure produce of any tea estate; they always blend manufactured tea in order to produce as delicate a flavour as possible. Still less, presumably, would they sell us wild tea! Nevertheless it might be an advantage to rediscover the original wild plant. In the everlasting search for the perfect tea-bush, giving greater yield, better flavour, and above all more resistance to disease, wild tea might have something to contribute. Good types of tea-bush are built up gradually by expert selection and crossing; particular qualities are built into them one by one. Breeding is not everything, but no cunning of manufacture can turn a poor quality tea-bush into a good one.

Apart from the obvious utilitarian object of making good tea better, the problem of the origin of a plant like *Camellia sinensis* is tantalizing to the geographical botanist. The unravelling of the tangled skein of evidence, incomplete as it is, is an enthralling exercise. Most people, who realize that the ceremony of tea-drinking has been carried on in China for three thousand years, naturally suppose that tea originated in China. So it may have done. But there is enough evidence—botanical, geographical, and even ethnological—to suggest that the art of making tea travelled not from east to west, but in the opposite direction. The first tea-drinkers may have lived on the borders of Assam, not in China at all. China has given us written records of tea-drinking from the earliest times, but none of the origin of the tea-plant. More primitive people of course could not furnish any written records at all.

Camellia sinensis is a plant of the foothills, not of the plains. Is it not significant how its cultivation, even its very existence, seems to cling around places where the much-travelled Tai race is, or has been, or could have been? The long road of their migrations is still bordered with tea-bushes. Will anyone claim that this is coincidence?

Some years ago my wife and I, starting from Tocklai Experimental Station, set out to explore the approaches to Dapha Bum from the west. It was already March. We had little hope of reaching even the lower slopes of the mountain so late in the season, and getting back before the rains came; but we might blaze the trail to a ridge.

In Sadiya we made all transport arrangements in advance: elephants to take us to the Kamlang River, dug-outs to take us up the swift water to the point where it emerges brawling from the hills, and Mishmi coolies to meet us there and carry on to the first highland village. It was a major problem to find two servants to accompany us, one of whom must be able to speak Mishmi. Finally we were saddled with two unreliables, one of them being a well-known thief.

Early in March we left Sadiya by lorry for the place where the elephants were to meet us and take us across the Kamlang River to Chongkham, a Hkamti Shan—that is to say, Tai—village on the far bank. Here our troubles began. The canoes were not yet assembled, and we had to wait a day; then we started up the river, which flowed swiftly now that the snow was melting on the mountains at its source. Progress was slow. By noon on the second day we reached water so swift that there was little hope of further progress by canoe. We camped where we were, and early the following morning tried again to make headway up the river, before the sun began to melt the snow. The water had fallen during the night, but not enough, and the boatmen could take us no farther.

Some Mishmi coolies turned up, and we were able to get along a few more miles, finally reaching the place where we had originally intended to disembark. Here wide banks of sand and boulders, which would be covered during the rainy season, offered unlimited camping ground. We were right at the foot of the hills, and the river came rushing out of a ravine. We camped again, waiting for more Mishmis to arrive.

Next day we started up the gorge, which was filled with lush jungle. The track was rough and rocky. Presently we had to cross the Kamlang River, now a raging, racing torrent, by a dangerously flimsy bamboo bridge. The Mishmi headman said they had built it especially for us, but obviously it was just as useful to them. The only alternative was a cane rope higher up the gorge—much safer, but out of our way.

A steep climb up a bold cliff brought us to the first village, where we slept the night; and a short march on the following day to a second village called Glo. No amount of argument or offers of higher pay would persuade the Mishmis to take us any farther; indeed, they said flatly there was nowhere farther to go. Our camping ground was a muddy hollow not far from two tumbledown huts.

Dapha Bum, near the head of the Kamlang valley, was about twelve miles distant as the crow flies, but invisible. Between us and it, on our side, a range of hills ran parallel with the river, and we thought that if we could reach the top of this ridge, some four thousand or five thousand feet above us, it would be as much as we could hope to accomplish this season. But as snow lay deep along the crest there was no hope of persuading the half-naked Mishmis to carry our loads, however light. Could we find a possible way up to this ridge? The altitude of our camp was barely four thousand feet, so, unless we climbed at least as much again, there was little chance of our finding any temperate plants.

As spring advanced the forest on the surrounding hills became dappled with a hundred colours, among which fountains of purple rhododendron blossom spouted up vividly. For the first fortnight or three weeks we simply collected round our camp. Not far away was Glo lake, a small oval basin scooped out of the hills, and this we visited several times; but it was not possible to walk round it—swamps and cane-brakes barred the way. We found a primitive bamboo raft tied to a tree. Free-

board was nil, but we eventually hired a crew of two to propel
us round the lake. In, or rather *on*, this clumsy vessel we
explored the channel by which the water flowed out, to tumble
hundreds of feet into the valley below, and we even in trepida-
tion crossed the lake. Had a violent storm blown up, as often
happens in these hills, we must, inevitably, have been in danger
of drowning.

The local Mishmis were a sullen crowd, and unco-operative.
We could not persuade them to do anything we wanted, least of
all to carry loads. We began to grow desperate. If we were ever
going to reach the top of the ridge we ought to start without
delay, though the weather continued bad. As the snow melted
on the ridge above us, and on the more distant range across the
deep valley which separates the Kamlang River from the Lohit,
we thought the coolies might take a more reasonable view. But
it was the opium season, and the women were all busy on the
cleared slopes, scratching the fat poppy capsules with bamboo
prongs, and wiping off the milky juice on to bits of cloth.

Not until we had been nearly four weeks in this camp did we
at last prevail on the villagers to undertake a reconnaissance
up the slope from the lake. They promised, sulkily, to clear a
small camping ground, as high up as possible; thence to cut a
path up the mountain. They would return after a few days and
report on the prospects of reaching the top.

Two or three men went off on this expedition, and we
awaited their return with the utmost impatience. What would
they have to report?

While we were still at Sadiya a planter friend, "Josh" Rey-
nolds, had turned up. He was a veteran flyer, and had a small
plane of his own. (In Assam a light plane is much more useful
than a light car, especially in the rains, and more than one
planter has come to realize it.) Josh's usual passenger for week-
ends flips round the foothills was another friend of ours, Nick
Warner, also a planter. Before he left Sadiya we invited Josh,
half seriously, to visit us in the Mishmi hills. "You might bring
us a mail! " we added.

He asked a few questions. "Where's your camp? What land-
marks are there? How long will you be there?"

"Follow the Kamlang River into the hills," I said, pointing to
the map. "Our camp will be near Glo lake, quite easy to find.
There'll be two tents." But knowing the terrible Mishmi hills, I

realized the hazards, and did not expect Josh to make the attempt.

"Everything depends on the weather," he said, as we studied the large-scale map. "Given good visibility, you can expect us."

That would certainly be fun, and something to look forward to. But the weather in the Mishmi hills is unpredictable. With its turbulent atmosphere, and poor visibility, it is no place for a light plane, and the weather ever since we left Sadiya had been atrocious, especially at week-ends. I had ceased to look out for Josh, or to think of his visit at all.

Since our arrival at Glo we seemed to have accomplished little. In four weeks I had not seen a single camellia. We could not stay much longer, for it was essential to get back before the rains broke, otherwise we might be cut off for several months, with no reserves of food.

It was our fifth week and a fine Sunday morning. We were not feeling energetic, so we decided to visit a near-by patch of forest where we had seen maples with bunches of enormous fruits. On the bank grew deliciously scented white begonias.

We climbed up the rough track, found our maple-trees, and cast round for some means of knocking off a branch or two bearing fruits.

Suddenly, with one accord, we stopped and glanced up.

"Listen! What's that?"

From behind the hill in the direction of Glo lake came a faint hum, the sort of noise a small dynamo makes, only fainter. Or possibly a distant plane. My wife was listening intently. Then her face lit up.

"Gosh! Josh! " she shouted, and started to run. I snatched off my bush hat and began to wave it to the trees, while running round madly in a circle seeking a gap in the canopy through which we might see a clear patch of sky. But it was impossible to see anything from where we were.

In a moment, as though somebody had opened a door, the noise became loud and unmistakable; the plane had come over the hill. It must be right overhead. We tore headlong down the path back to camp, stumbling over rocks, tripping over roots, anxious only to arrive in time. The noise of the plane rose and fell more clearly than ever, as it dropped and circled. We reached the open, and could see up and down the Kamlang

valley, and the mountains across the river. Only a stout cattle
fence separated us from the tents. As we scrambled over it we
glanced to the left. The little plane was straightening out for
a clear run down the gorge. At that moment it was still just
ahead of us. We shouted and yelled in our excitement, waved
scarves, hats, handkerchiefs—a few seconds later it was level
with us. It passed hardly higher than the camp, and within five
or six hundred yards. One more circuit and the pilot must have
seen us. The muted hum of the plane, our momentary link with
civilization, died slowly, became faint, ceased.

If only we had spent that Sunday morning in camp!

Josh's plane had come straight in to the hills over Glo lake,
picked up our tents without difficulty, circled them twice a few
hundred feet up, dropped a packet of newspapers, and made its
exit by the Kamlang Gorge. In our little camp was assembled
the entire population of the village who were not working in the
fields—six or eight persons. Our servants had just gathered up
the scattered papers and put them in our tent. Every one was
talking. We were still a little out of breath after our mad run.
The episode had boosted our morale; but it would have boosted
it to the skies if we had only been on the spot, and could have
waved to our friends as they swooped across, the propeller
almost fanning our faces.

Now the Mishmis—men, women and children—gathered
round the entrance to our tent, an unusual experience for us.
Hitherto they had shown neither curiosity nor interest in us,
much less friendliness. One or two seemed to be trying to
smile. All this attention was so unexpected that we were em-
barrassed.

"We've become V.I.P.'s overnight," my wife remarked,
solemnly shaking hands with a little girl.

Prestige! That was it! Few, if any of them, had ever seen or
heard a plane in their lives. And now a plane had actually
visited their village and dropped a package into our camp.
Surely this might help things along!

It did. When the headman returned the next day he was unusually polite, and quickly showed that he really did mean to
help. In fact, we were misled by his account of the path they had
cut up the flank of the ridge, and saw ourselves reaching unexpected heights; but at the worst it was worth while making the
trip. Speed was essential, for only a week's supplies remained.

A group of Paphiopedalum wardii, growing as the author first discovered them in North Burma

Below: *Another slipper orchid—Paphiopedalum villosum. Originally found near Moulmein in Southern Burma, it was re-discovered by the author many hundreds of miles farther north*

The Chinese coffin-tree (Taiwania cryptomerioides) growing tidily in the Maymyo Botanic Garden, Burma

We decided to spend two clear days in the new camp, and coolies were promised for the following day.

A scarcely visible track through the forest brought us to the north end of the lake which lay between us and the ridge, where we turned at right angles to begin the ascent. It was not steep here, and the coolies had cut a broad track. We got along well. But all too soon we reached a clearing less than a thousand feet above the lake, and were told we must camp here—there wasn't any water higher up. As this is one of the wettest corners of Assam, it seemed strange. But the heavy rainfall of the Mishmi hills cuts deep ravines, so that when ascending a ridge it is all too often impossible to find water within reach.

That same evening I explored a near-by gulley, whence we drew our water. Here I found our first camellia. Nor was it just any camellia; it was definitely a form of *C. sinensis*, and as I thought at the time—and think still—very probably wild tea! No one could ever have cultivated tea in this jungle. Moreover, it was just what one would expect truly wild Assam tea to look like, a small solitary tree with tea-leaves. Unfortunately, there were neither flowers nor fruits.

We had brought with us on the expedition a single bottle of port for great occasions. Perhaps this was a great occasion, so we decided to open it that evening. At any rate we had had no reason to do so before. We got out the tumblers and a cork-screw. Everything was ready. I was just warming it slightly over the oil stove when there came a sharp *ping*, and the whole bottom dropped off the bottle as though it had been opened by pressing a spring. It was quite remarkable how swiftly the port slipped out like a large bubble!

Next morning we started up the ridge. The Mishmis had been as good as their word, and really had worked hard. At the out-set they had literally had to tunnel a passage through a belt of cane-brake. A cane-brake in tropical East Asia does not mean a stand of bamboos, troublesome as that is, but a far worse obstacle; the horribly prickly lower stems of a climbing palm, the toughest of all tropical lianas, set as close as they can grow. Once through this, for hour after hour we slogged up this un-promising ridge without finding what we sought. But shortly before we turned back—still far from the top—we found on a fallen tree-trunk an epiphytic rhododendron and an Agapetes, the latter in flower. Then, nearing the camp, we saw something we had missed on the way up. This was a shrub, a species of Euonymus bearing the most enormous fruits I have ever seen on a spindle-tree. They were as large as walnuts, suspended by pedicels which were flattened to look like narrow ribbon, or braid. They were nearly ripe, because within a day or two of being gathered they began to split open and display the brilliant scarlet and orange seeds. It is hardly possible to exaggerate the splendour of such a bush when fully ripe. But it was a curious season for a spindle to be in fruit; rather should it be in flower, though it was really too early for that. It was, in fact, mid-season for spindle-trees.

The walk back to Glo set the final seal on our little expedition with a dramatic discovery. We had reached the end of the lake, where there grew many fine trees, including some beautiful laurels. Descending a sharp incline, I looked up and noticed directly in front of me a smallish tree bearing a number of fruits the size of crab-apples. As so often happens with trees on a slope, I had not noticed it on the way up.

There was something about this tree which attracted my immediate attention. I climbed up and collected all the fruits I could find—there were not many of them—and could hardly believe my eyes when I discovered that they were not crab-apples, but the three-celled fruits of a camellia-like plant, apple-cheeked and perhaps no more than half ripe. But what astonished me was their incredible size. What would they look like when ripe and beginning to crack open? There was no certainty that this was tea, or even a camellia at all; but if not, it was something very closely related. I would have given a lot to see it in flower. No doubt, like tea itself, it flowers in November or December. Had there been flowers one could have named it, and seen just where it fitted into the scheme of tea. On the other hand, if the fruits had been ripe we could have raised plants at Tocklai. All this shows how unsatisfactory these short expeditions can be. As things are, all we have—besides the knowledge that by Glo lake there exists a remarkable camellia-like tree —are some pressed leaves and some half-ripe fruits preserved in spirit. And this within a few days' march of the plains.

And that was the end of our reconnaissance towards Dapha Bum. Within a day of our return to Glo camp we packed up, and willing coolies carried our loads down through the Kamlang Gorge. No trace of the temporary bridge remained, and we crossed the turbulent river one at a time in a sort of cane rabbit hutch, which, suspended by a handle at either end from the cane rope, was laboriously pulled across.

In due course we reached the edge of the plain. The water here was far too rough for canoes, and on a blistering hot day we walked the fourteen miles to Karim. In the middle of this march my wife startled me by suddenly walking into the Kamlang River fully dressed, boots and all, and sitting down right under the water! She emerged with dripping hair, and explained that she wasn't bent on committing suicide, only on staving off heat-stroke!

It had not been a very satisfactory journey, having fallen far short of its objective. But at least the Mishmi hills had lived up to their reputation for strange plants, of which not the least strange was the large-fruited camellia. The large-fruited Euonymus was a close second.

·14·

Musk goes off the Air

FEW plants have had a more dramatic rise to fame, or come a more ignominious cropper, than *Mimulus moschatus*—the once-popular and well-beloved musk. When I was a boy it was still everybody's plant, though I have no very clear recollection of the scent. To-day it is nobody's plant.

In our small front garden there was a bed with an edging of musk; it was circular, and in the centre grew a clump of unimaginative and somewhat featureless evergreen shrubs. There was also a fuchsia dripping crimson and violet flowers like bright tears, which I thought very striking. I was told it came from South America, and no doubt for that reason I would have called it intriguing, had the word been in vogue then.

But it was the border of musk which *made* the bed. We grew musk as a matter of course, because every one did. We lived at Cooper's Hill, in the country, and every cottage garden on Englefield Green had its patch or border of musk, or at least a window-box. It was as common, as popular, and almost as insignificant as mignonette. But it was cheap, easy to grow, and pretty in a trivial way. The village general shop sold musk-seed in penny packets, the envelope decorated with a coloured picture of larger and brighter musk-flowers than I ever saw in any garden. But nobody minded that. Everybody hoped that their plants too would reach such perfection.

The musk-plant came in more or less with the monkey-puzzle, though from the opposite end of the New World. (Actually it was discovered thirty years later, by which time the monkey-puzzle was a fair-sized tree.) But one associates both of them with mid-Victorian England. It was found by David Douglas on the banks of the Columbia River in 1826, long before the Gold Rush to California began; it went out when the lights went out over Europe. At the time of Douglas's discovery one didn't cross the American continent by train in a matter of days; or even by covered wagon in a matter of months. Unless engaged in fur-trading, one didn't cross it at all. To reach California or British Columbia you went by sea round Cape Horn and landed on the Pacific coast. Douglas left London in July 1824, and reached the mouth of the Columbia River in April 1825. The empty heart of the continent had not yet begun to beat.

The musk-plant first appeared in the Chiswick garden of the Horticultural Society of London, having been raised from seed collected by Douglas. Nowhere in his diary did he comment on its scent. This omission may be significant. In spite of all appearance to the contrary, Douglas did not publish the name *Mimulus moschatus*. The plant was first described and illustrated by John Lindley in the *Botanical Register*, Vol. 13, pl. 1118 (1828) from a Chiswick plant, and the fact that he attached Douglas's name to it as the authority seemed to be simply courtesy on Lindley's part until Mr W. T. Stearn discovered Douglas's unpublished notes in 1936. The one relating to our plant (see *Journal of the Royal Horticultural Society, London*, Vol. 77, p. 291; 1952) is as follows: "*Mimulus moschatus: caule repente foliisque glanduloso-villosis, foliis ovatis dentatis, pedunculis folio brevioribus.* On the margins of grassy springs and when trodden on emits a powerful odour of musk. Flowers yellow, small, continuing through the greater part of the summer. Not infrequent around Fort Vancouver."

Whether all the plants raised at Chiswick were scented or not is doubtful. Certainly one was, but probably not all. One of the scented plants was picked out, and it made such an impression on the Council of the Society that they took the precaution of propagating it by cuttings. In fact, for many years all *M. moschatus* was reproduced in this way. The true scented musk of commerce was a clone of the original plant. It was not till the demand began vastly to exceed the supply that this plant was raised on a commercial scale from seed. From that moment, no doubt, the scent began to wane.

There is nothing in the record to suggest that outside the Royal Horticultural Society of London itself the new plant created any particular furore at that stage. After all, it's nothing much to look at—a modest herbaceous perennial a few inches tall, with commonplace pouting flowers of a rather crude yellow. It would be unlikely to fire the imagination of gardeners in those days—and why should it in these?—unless it possessed some secret weapon. It quickly proved to have several amiable qualities: it came easily from seed, like the proverbial mustard and cress, it continued to flower all the summer, and it seeded itself everywhere, coming up between the cobbles in the yard and the flagstones of the terrace; and it was stolidly hardy.

But what else? Surely these rather homely virtues are not everywhere regarded as an infallible passport to immortality? Why, then, was musk for fifty years so much the fashion that it was grown by both rich and poor in the days when England was full of great houses with splendid gardens—now, alas, almost as extinct as musk itself? And why has it for another fifty years been so completely out of favour that to-day it is hard to find at all?

The answer is that *Mimulus moschatus*, as originally known, did indeed possess a secret weapon which couldn't be kept secret; something which neither the little blue border lobelia nor any other equally small plant in circulation to-day possesses; a pleasant and pervasive fragrance. This arose not from the flowers but from the whole plant, and particularly from the leaves. And an unusual scent it was too.

Scent is an elusive quality; it defies accurate description, still less accurate comparison. We do not so much experience it as become conscious of it. Mysteriously, it can conjure up an association of incongruous ideas, and project into our brains long-forgotten scenes in a muddled sequence, and a profound nostalgia may be provoked by a breath of scent of which we are hardly aware. Kipling knew this when he wrote: "Scent is quicker than sight or sound to make the heartstrings crack." But every one knows how impossible it is to describe scents, or even to recall clearly what they were like.

Obvious animal scents are not very common in the plant world, although a correspondent to a gardening journal once claimed to recognize seventeen plants and thirteen animals smelling of musk! However, I am not convinced that a sharp line can be drawn between animal scents and plant scents. Both are the result of chemical substances, which can be analysed and finally made synthetically by the chemist.

But it is useless to apply mathematical axioms to such matters, and to argue that things which are equal to the same thing must always be equal to one another; they are, of course, in geometry, but not in everyday life. You might suspect that if seventeen plants and thirteen animals smell of the same thing they must all smell alike. But you would be wrong. Scent is much too subtle to be so accurately assessed. Species of Amorphophallus and Aristolochia both smell of rotten meat without smelling in the least like one another; but the imitation is good enough to deceive bluebottles, which no doubt are moronic creatures anyway. Of course the smell of rotten meat is really due to the breakdown of proteins by bacteria, thereby releasing noxious gases; it is not inherent in the meat itself, still less in the live animal; it is a product of decay. Rather in the same way, when plant scents are analysed, they turn out to be complex mixtures of essential oils with a formula which no one but an organic chemist is on speaking terms with. It is coming to be thought that they are waste products, more or less injurious to plant life, so that they are scaled off in cells out of harm's way—that, at least, is one view.

But even waste products can be turned to good account, and many plants make indirect use of theirs to attract insects which, in searching for the scent, pollinate the flowers. This applies notably to night-scented flowers, and to those which smell of carrion. (We have all seen insects visiting scentless flowers by day, where there are the certain attractions of honey or pollen.)

The success story of the musk-plant is clearly due to the fact that its scent had a universal appeal, and many people have borne witness that on a warm summer's day it was strong and pleasant.

Compared with the powerful odour of real musk, that of the musk-plant is extremely delicate. Personally I can recall the odour of musk more readily than I can that of the musk-plant, which was a mere shadow of it. But by the time I saw and smelt animal musk myself I had almost forgotten what the musk-plant smelt like.

The male musk-deer of the Himalayas and the high mountains of western China carries a small spherical pouch about the size of a golf ball beneath the skin but outside the body cavity, near the genital organs; its biological use is to attract the female. I never saw this small animal alive, but the Tibetan hunters used to bring the pods, as these pouches are called, into the village where I was living to sell to the Chinese merchants—the price at that time (1911) was something like twenty shillings an ounce, and each pod contained about one ounce of musk. I was often present in the room—a small, low wooden-walled apartment with latticed windows covered with coarse paper—when the little sacs were slit open, tested for purity, emptied, and weighed; the scraped skins themselves were put in one receptacle, the dark-brown moist powder, the musk itself, in another. While the inevitable haggling over price took place the scent pervaded the room; it was strong, and over-sweet almost to the point of bitterness, as saccharine is almost bitter compared with sugar. In those days musk was in demand by European perfumers as a fixative for their scents, and nearly all of it was exported. It is still in demand, even at its present price of about sixteen pounds per ounce.

Comparing the smell in that Chinese village room with my recollection of the musk round the bed in the garden of my childhood, I realize that neither scent is describable except in terms of the other; and neither makes the same impact on the memory, that, for instance, a rich colour makes. Musk scent gives birth in me nowadays to a faint nostalgia for the alps of Yunnan, and, by association of ideas, recalls my first sight of blue poppies growing wild. Few people, I suppose, have ever smelt fresh animal musk, and their comparison of the musk-plant with it—if they have ever smelt that either—is second-hand, or perhaps based on the perfumer's art.

And then suddenly, in our gardens, the scent of musk went out like a lamp! It was not sudden really—it had been growing weaker for years; what was sudden was the realization that it had definitely gone, and people then lamented what they had lost. This, as near as one can judge, happened about the year 1912 or a little later—just before the First World War. And worse was to follow.

If the plant had lost its delicate scent in the concentration-camps of cultivation, of course, more could be imported and the scent restored. Alas, inquiries presently set on foot showed that this mimulus had lost its scent in British Columbia, in California, and all other parts of North America west of the Rockies, its original home. In fact, everywhere. It was a universal visitation. Millions who had never seen—or at least never grown—musk, heard the wail go up to heaven and read the obituary notices.

The Press took up this curious botanical episode, and bogus theories and ill-considered opinions received a publicity they did not deserve, and a credence of which they were unworthy. To put the matter in headlines: one summer there was musk. Gardens and window-boxes throughout the country were gay with it. Rooms filled with its gentle fragrance. The warm bright summer days were drowsy with the hum of insects round it. The next summer it had vanished. Nobody grew musk any more. It had lost its scent for ever.

It was not as though the hybridizers had got to work on it. Musk was still (when they could find any) the same cheerful but rather dowdy little yellow-flowcred 'Scroph' they had always known as "the monkey-flower." Roses might lose their fragrance when they got into the clutches of the hybridizer; but one did not mind that so much—they were still beautiful. But the charm of musk lay entirely in its scent; when it lost that it lost everything. And having lost everything, poor musk sprang into instant posthumous fame. Too late the public realized what it too had lost—that unique perfume which had brought the small sallow flower a million lovers. For half a century nobody had spoken of it, but everybody had grown it. By the time nobody grew it, every one was talking about it.

What was now referred to as "the lost scent of musk" was a major subject of discussion. Why? why? people asked. The gardening Press entered into the fray, and their correspondence columns scintillated with startling ideas. Many correspondents put forward theories more ingenious than profound. It wasn't musk which had lost its scent, they said, but man who had lost the power of smelling it! Valiant efforts were made to correlate the departed scent of musk with the coming of the motor-car about the year 1910, when the stink of petrol on the roads was becoming familiar.

It might perhaps have occurred to the author of this particular solecism that if man's sense of smell had become so vitiated by the spreading fumes of petrol that he could no longer detect the fragrance of musk it was at least unlikely that he could register *any* scents. Roses, jasmine, and honeysuckle would also be scentless. Yet so far they were not. A half-hearted attempt was made to prove that cherry-pie (heliotrope) was losing its fragrance. But if that was true forty years ago it has made a remarkable come-back since, in spite of the introduction of petrol-driven machines into the garden itself. It was also pointed out by hard-headed botanists that whatever milestone 1910 might mark in the evolution of the motor-car, it did not suddenly mark the loss of fragrance in musk, which had been gradually losing its strength for thirty years—that is, ever since 1880. The year 1910 merely marked a sudden awareness among the public of what had occurred.

It is well known that civilized man's sense of smell is sadly deficient compared with that of his uncivilized contemporaries, since he is far less dependent on it than they are; but it is still quite good enough to give him pleasure in fragrance, and it can be much improved by training. The perfume chemist can as easily detect a whiff of musk, if present, as a tea-taster can detect the slightest contamination in the manufacture of tea. So the theory that man's nose was drowned in the rising tide of petrol fumes was quickly demolished.

Another theory gaily put forward without benefit of fact was that the musk-plant had never *had* any scent. The scent resided in an organism which lived in symbiosis with it, and with the universal extinction of this symbiotic junior partner had gone the scent. But both partners in a symbiotic relationship can usually be detected, at least with the aid of a microscope. There had been no suggestion of symbiosis when musk was a popular plant; and the author of this theory was at no pains to identify his brain-child. It could hardly be a mycorrhizal infection, since musk grew with ease in almost any soil. Anyhow, its almost universal extinction would require some explanation. How had its liquidation been effected with so little fuss, and with no inconvenience to the senior partner, which continued to flourish wonderfully on its own? If the scented and unscented plants were merely forms of one species, clearly the unscented was as well off as the other.

Quite early in the *post-mortem* one or two botanists who were acquainted with the facts had already suggested a simple solution of the mystery. Musk, they said, had not lost its scent, but the scented *form* of musk had been lost. In other words, the scented musk of the Columbia River was a sport or even a hybrid. It cropped up occasionally, but whenever it did so it tended to disappear equally quickly, no doubt by promiscuous crossing with the far more abundant unscented form.

With this suggestion the pieces of the puzzle began to fall

into place, and bit by bit a coherent picture emerged. Douglas's silence concerning any scent, the unexplained decision of the Horticultural Society to propagate vegetatively and spread the clone, the slow decline in fragrance over the years, the occasional re-appearance of the scented form both in its old home and its new—all began to make sense now.

Douglas, without realizing it, had collected seed of both forms, and both forms came up. The plant's greatest value lay in the scented one. This had been at once recognized by the Horticultural Society, who isolated it, propagated it by cuttings, and thus distributed the clone. So the scented form got off to a good start.

For half a century this form, which continued to be reproduced vegetatively, prevailed, giving pleasure to every one. Unfortunately, when the plant began to be raised from seed the ordinary unscented form came up too, and when the demand for scented musk became overwhelming people grew careless about the correct propagation of their most powerfully scented plants. They had recourse to raising it from seed—all the more difficult to control because the plant seeded itself wherever it was grown. So dilution began. If, as seems probable, a generation passed before people woke up to what had happened, it only proves that the scented form was not easy to put down altogether.

For some years after musk had ceased to smell like musk, odd plants of the scented form appeared here and there, both in England and in America. Nor would it be surprising if these sporadic appearances were to continue indefinitely, at least in the plant's original home, though it may seldom be recorded over such a wide and sparsely populated area. If the above solution of the mystery is correct it would, on the contrary, be surprising if the scented form finally and utterly disappeared, never to return.

Nevertheless, as Dr Balfour Gourlay pertinently observed, if it really was a chance scented variety which Douglas unwittingly collected among millions of unscented plants, this was a much more remarkable fact than its subsequent disappearance. Unless it was specially preserved, its ultimate extinction was practically inevitable. There seems to be only one slight difficulty in accepting this suggestion. If the scented form is a sport, would it come true from seed? We know it was raised from seed sent from Vancouver, in the State of Washington, but that gives away nothing as to its parentage. No doubt, then, it was a chance seedling.

There is, of course, a possibility that the scented musk could be restored to us. All we have to do, presumably, is to wait till a scented plant turns up—and an intensive search along the banks of the Columbia River should not be difficult to organize —and pounce on it. It would then only be necessary to propagate it by cuttings to work up a stock. But do we really want it back? Perhaps it has had its day.

Though the sad story of the musk-plant enshrines the name of David Douglas, his fame rests on surer foundations. It was Douglas who first introduced into this country the Oregon grape (*Mahonia aquifolium*), the Californian poppy (*Eschscholzia californica*), the red flowering-currant (*Ribes sanguineum*), *Limnanthes douglasii*, *Lupinus polyphyllus*, *Rubus nutkanus*, and the fabulous conifers of the Pacific coast of North America, not the least of which is still known as the Douglas Fir (*Pseudotsuga menziesii*), which in its home reaches three hundred feet. As long as trees are grown in Great Britain and Europe these magnificent "Douglases" will keep his memory green.

Musk Plant
(*Mimulus moschatus*)

·15·

And Some fell by the Wayside

THE introduction of a new foreign plant into England consists of three distinct steps. First, there is the discovery of the plant. Secondly, there is the active introduction—the collecting and dispatch of seeds, bulbs, cuttings, or even of entire plants, to England. That also is part of the plant-hunter's job, and calls for judgment and a lot of hard work: collecting, drying, cleaning, and packing his finds, and making dried specimens for the herbarium to help in identification. If, after all that, the seeds do not germinate or the bulbs are rotten, or the plants have dried out, it is probably his fault. He has failed at the second step.

Lastly, there is the sowing of the seeds, and the raising and maintenance of the young plants; and so long as the seeds, bulbs, or roots arrive in good condition, the plant-hunter has done all he can towards final success. He cannot blame himself for failure after that. Now it is some one else's responsibility.

Once a good plant has been discovered, its exact location is known and recorded—or ought to be. I think I could give detailed directions which would enable anyone to find the plants mentioned in this book. Whenever I found a plant which was worth cultivating I noted in detail where I had found it and how to get there, when it flowers, and the best time to secure seed of it. The plant-hunter who does that has successfully performed the first part of his task. Yet it is natural that he should experience a feeling of failure if he does not complete the second step, though in fact many a first-class plant has been found by one man (not necessarily a plant-hunter) and later introduced by another. However, it is the introducer who gets most of the credit, which is one reason for a plant-hunter's disappointment when he fails to introduce a good discovery. Still, that is no reason for keeping the locality of his plant to himself!

If, however, he not only finds a good plant, but also completes the second step, and then the young plants do not live to flower, or, having flowered once, fail to set seed before they die, he still feels that he has been cheated. This is understandable, even if illogical. But there it is. Nothing is quite so satisfactory for him as finding and introducing a first-class hardy plant which presently becomes popular.

Who introduced the horse-chestnut? The first crocus? Or wallflowers? Every plant-lover ought to know the names of these benefactors; they should be immortal, but nobody knows who they were.

If I were asked what one plant above all others I would choose to have introduced into England I would say, without hesitation, gorse; only that happens to be a native plant already.

I cannot recall a single journey on which I did not have cause to lament the omission of several plants because I failed to get seed. Either I did not return to the same place in the autumn, and did not find the plants elsewhere; or I returned too early and collected unripe seed, or too late and collected no seed at all. But some plants I simply could not find again, or did not recognize in winter dress.

All these things happened to me during my early expeditions. Later failures were due rather to misfortunes at the other end; and few things are more discouraging than to send home seeds which germinate freely, only to die as seedlings. One thing which is even more distressing, however, is to watch a beautiful plant flower, and sit by its bedside while it slowly dies, childless, knowing it to be the last of its kind in Europe. When it finally disappears the species is lost to cultivation, and all is to do again.

Campanula calcicola is—was—one of the most delightful little rock-plants imaginable. It has everything. It owes its charm, not to a single feature, but to all features—a compact, well-proportioned figure, graceful leaves, delicate bells which nestle close above them, nodding on short wiry stems, and a striking blend of colours: pale hyacinth-blue flowers against rifle-green leaves inlaid with malachite. For the leaves are unusual—reniform, or kidney-shaped, dark green with light-green veins, like inlay work. It is an elfin work of art.

I first noticed *Campanula calcicola* growing at the top of the pass when crossing the limestone range which separates the Yungning basin from the Litang River in Szechwan. It was August, and the plant was in full bloom. It must have been rare; at least, I never saw it anywhere else. Moreover, it had been collected a year or two before by one of Forrest's men, but had not yet been introduced. That was curious for such a gem of a plant, and could only be accounted for by its comparative rarity; also, no doubt, the difficulty of recognizing shrivelled plants in the winter.

I marked my plants very carefully. On a cold windy day, when the sky was heavily overcast, I recrossed the pass on my way back to Talifu, and, thanks to the cairns I had built, found the bleached plants, shrivelled to almost nothing. I don't think there can have been very much seed, judging by the small number of plants I saw. Some of it had already fallen. Nevertheless what there was reached England safely, was sown, germinated, and flowered in 1922 or 1923. A pot-plant was exhibited at one of the summer shows of the Royal Horticultural Society, and a photograph of it appeared in *Gardening Illustrated*.

Within a year or two it was dead, and the species was extinct in Britain. I have never seen it since, wild or cultivated; but I could find it again on that savage limestone range.

Another plant which was successfully introduced and cultivated for a time is *Cyananthus wardii*. I saw a beautiful specimen of it flowering under glass at Sir Frederick Stern's Sussex home. One would think that, coming from a high altitude in Tibet, it would be hardy enough to stand up to any weather we could provide out of doors in England. And so it would be, no doubt, if ability to withstand cold were all. But hardiness involves much more than that. The temperature must be not only right for a plant to thrive, but right at the right time; whether it is for the germination of the seeds, the opening of the flowers, or the ripening of the fruit. And the relative humidity of the air is not less important than maximum and minimum temperatures. The benefits of snow cover in winter are also difficult to provide in the absence of snow. No doubt it disliked living in glass-houses; but what could one do to preserve the thing?

Its large periwinkle-blue flowers are fringed with long glistening hairs, like sealskin; so thickly do they grow in the throat of the corolla tube that they form a white plug.

Cyananthus wardii is an alpine. We had greater success with another species from a lower altitude which I collected the same year. This grows in meadows and round the edges of barley fields and other rough cultivation, a long lanky scrambler with very large flowers the colour of Parma violets. But no Cyananthus is ever likely to be a popular plant in Great Britain. The genus appears to be cursed with a delicate constitution, and all too easily succumbs to the peculiarities of our climate. Several of them are delightful rock-plants, but they are mainly for the connoisseur who can lavish attention on their frail constitutions.

The two plants just mentioned had at least the will to flower once in an alien land, and show us what they are like. But not all introductions have been so patient. There is, for example, the painful story of *Meconopsis speciosa*. I well remember my incredulous amazement when I first caught sight of that beautiful prickly blue poppy.

The village of Atuntzu stands at the head of a stony valley nearly ten thousand feet above sea-level, on the flank of the Mekong–Yangtze divide. Immediately above the village the mountains rise to sixteen thousand or seventeen thousand feet, consisting of razor-sharp ridges and jagged peaks. Here and there a small pool occupies a rock basin tucked in among the barren cliffs and long screes sloping steeply down to the stream.

I often climbed there, and, when I reached the last of the tree fringe, would continue up over the bare slopes, looking for alpine plants. Early one fine summer morning I found myself well up the mountain, with nearly the whole day before me. I had an idea of searching for a little-used pass reported to cross the range hereabouts. Presently I found myself on a scree composed of large angular blocks with sharp edges. I was higher on this range than I had ever been before, and revelled in the keen air, and the magnificent scenery. But this rough scree was practically barren. There was no soil on the surface, and few plants were tall enough to grow up through the loose rocks.

When, therefore, looking across the rugged slope, I saw at a little distance a flash of shining azure blue, I was curious. At first I thought it must be a flower; but I quickly realized how impossible that was; there was no plant visible in any direction. It must be a blue stone. But what? Copper sulphate? Neverthe-

The extraction of coffin-planks from the remote jungles of North Burma,
by river and mule transport

It is not only the timber of the coffin-tree that is beautiful. The tree is worth growing for its graceful foliage alone

less I continued to stare at it; indeed, I could not take my eyes
off it. What a heavenly blue! What mineral could give such a
colour, and in such a place! Had I made a real discovery of
the first importance? Very slowly I turned my eyes away and
began to scan the scree in every direction, staring hard. My eyesight, I knew, was pretty good. Yes, surely there it was again, a
little farther away; and there too, off to the right—no—yes! I
hardly dared move. I wanted to solve the puzzle where I stood,
before—— a wild belief was slowly forming in my mind. No, it
couldn't be, it was quite impossible. But the idea persisted, refused to be dislodged. Was, *was* my first thought right—*was* it a
flower? I still stood on the same spot, my gaze wandering round
the crags, close now, and across the intervening ranges to the
great indigo blank which marked the Mekong Gorge, with the
snowy range of Ka-Karpo (Kagurpu) rising like a white cathedral behind it. And so my gaze slowly came back to the
immediate scene, and I looked down at my feet: there, in a
crevice within a yard of me, was the most bewitching blue
flower I had ever seen—several blooms on a long raceme! So,
incredibly, it *was* a flower, the first blue poppy I had ever encountered—but I knew instinctively that it could only be that.

My reactions to this find were extremely human. Of course I
believed that I had discovered a new plant, and an unusually
fine one. I wrote a long description of it to Arthur Bulley, for
whom I was then working, and sent it by runner a ten-day trip
to the nearest post office; naturally the story lost nothing in the
telling. In due course he replied, and his letter made it obvious
that there had been considerable correspondence about my
Meconopsis. Some one had suggested that it might be *M.
speciosa*, a plant which George Forrest had recently found in
Yunnan; but not everybody thought so, least of all Forrest, who
was in Edinburgh at the time. In fact, Bulley in his letter quoted
him as saying that it was most unlikely I had found *M. speciosa.*
"Ward's plant is probably a form of *M. rudis* or *M. racemosa*,"
he wrote to Bulley, who passed it all on to me for my
information.

In further letters I referred several times to my Meconopsis,
and in a later letter Bulley wrote: "Forrest is frantically resign-
ing himself to the belief that your poppy *is M. speciosa.*"

To return to that wonderful July day above Atuntzu: I found
half a dozen large plants in good bloom. All thoughts of search-

ing for the pass were abandoned; I spent the time searching for *M. speciosa* instead. In the afternoon I returned to my quarters in the village, tired but very pleased with myself. I reckoned I had climbed to fifteen thousand feet; no one was with me.

In late autumn I planned the round of trips for collecting seed, and when the first snow crested the Mekong–Yangtze divide I crossed the unknown pass, collecting plenty of *speciosa* seed on the way. It was the year the Chinese revolutionists rose against the Manchu dynasty, and this created chaos along the China–Tibetan border. But though I lost a large collection of photographic negatives in the disorganized post, my seed collection, which I took out with me to Burma, got through safely.

Back in England I learned something of the story of *Meconopsis speciosa*. I don't know whether Forrest had failed as yet to collect seed of this beautiful plant, or whether his seed had simply refused to germinate. At any rate, it was not yet in cultivation. Hence his dismay when I butted in and threatened to introduce it first.

However, my luck was no better than his. If my seed germinated at all, the seedlings did not thrive. So Forrest had another chance; he went back to his beloved Yunnan when I came home; and when I too returned to Yunnan I also tried again. But though on one or two occasions seeds actually germinated, the seedlings were always lost in the second year.

Thus *Meconopsis speciosa* remains to this day one of those which fell by the wayside.

But no plant I have ever seen in the mountains tantalized me so much as a certain dwarf rhododendron growing at the top of a cliff on the Assam frontier. It was May 10 when we reached our first camp up the gorge of the Di Chu. Silver fir and Tsuga formed the main forest canopy, but there were broad-leafed trees growing beneath them, notably rhododendrons of several species; also one of the most beautiful little cherries I have ever come across.

The altitude was about seven thousand feet, and at this point the Di Chu was a fearsome cataract. On the opposite side of the river an almost perpendicular cliff rose for several hundred feet, and, as one might expect, was practically bare. Near the summit, however, its brow was bound with stunted forest. So near was the cliff, and so high, I lay almost on my back, my head propped against a tree-trunk, and through a good field-glass scanned the top, to see if I could spot any interesting plants.

Almost immediately I was rewarded. In joints and cracks of the face, and forming a fringe where the cliff sloped back gently, and was covered with forest, grew a bushy shrub. It was in flower, and the flowers were a delicious deep pink like almond-blossom. Nor did it take long to convince myself that it could only be a dwarf rhododendron. Long and earnestly I looked at it, changing the point of view, raking the cliff up and down and across for every bush I could find, and staring for minutes at a time.

Next morning (and again on our way back a few days later) I continued to stare at that plant without learning anything more about it. What sort of dwarf rhododendron, almond-blossom pink, grows at about 7500 feet, flowering in May? I kept asking myself this question.

I tried to work out a route up the cliff, which was impossible, or a route up through the forest to the level of the top, and then across and down to the most get-at-able plant; and that indeed might have been possible. But what was utterly impossible was to cross the Di Chu. It was equally hopeless to get up the other side of the gorge, if we crossed the river near our base camp. I studied the problem for a long time, going carefully over the ground through my field-glasses, but could come to only one conclusion: I must find the plant on our side of the river.

Unfortunately, we had only a very few days here, and there was a great deal to collect. My wife worked heroically pressing the many specimens we collected, and we both searched madly for the wanted rhododendron, without success. The fact is, conditions of light and shade, drought and wetness, and other things, were so different on the two sides of the gorge that it was very unlikely the rhododendron grew on our side at all. Anyway if it did we never found it. This was a real failure, because we saw the plant in flower, mocking our efforts to reach it, and got neither herbarium specimen nor seed. I still dream of it sometimes and wonder what it was: *Lapponicum* type? *Saluense* type? *Anthopogon* type? or something unknown?

It would be easy enough to continue the harrowing tale—a tale of plants which have displayed themselves to us once in all the pride of their bloom, and then departed childless from the stage; of plants which here have grown for a time, then pined away and died without flowering, disliking what little they have seen of their new world; and of plants whose seeds did not even germinate. But of all the motley throng, I am most interested in those I saw growing wild, but of which no seed ever reached England.

There was that beautiful Astilbe with long catkins of white blossom, seen once only in the high and hostile mountains of the Assam frontier; the nigger-brown clematis of Hkinlum, in North Burma, which opened its first flowers in late November. They were startling flowers—large, fluorescent, mahogany-brown by reflected light, but amethyst when you looked straight through them, the big creamy white stamens as motionless as carved ivory.

One of the most unexpected plants I ever found was *Chamae-periclymenum wardii*, in the Nam Tamai valley of North Burma, a dwarf creeping-plant like *Chamaepericlymenum suecicum* and *C. canadense* (more familiar to most people as *Cornus suecica* and *C. canadensis*). The seeds germinated, but the war broke out in the same year, and their fate was sealed. This, however, was no great loss to horticulture, so far as one can judge, unless a tendency on the part of the bracts to turn red could have been encouraged. A dwarf Cornus the colour of *Cornus florida rubra* would certainly have been something out of the common.

It is good to keep alive the memory of departed spirits, which is my excuse for writing these obituary notices. They will serve to remind the next generation that there still is work to be done, and it is to our successors that we must reveal where these missing plants can be found.

Horticultural know-how also improves. Fifty years ago no one could grow primulas of the Petiolares section. The wonderful *P. sonchifolia*, extolled by collectors in highland Burma and Yunnan for years, resisted every effort at cultivation, though everybody had a shot at it. To-day it is almost a commonplace in the mild damp west; at least, it is grown with comparative ease. The electrically heated, thermostatically controlled soil-boxes now in use in greenhouses have revolutionized the possibilities of germination.

Thus I end on a hopeful note. And, after all, why not? The real marvel is not that a few plants have failed in our country, but that so many, from all parts of the world, thrive.

Geography and Living Standards in South-east Asia

by

the late Frank Kingdon-Ward
O.B.E., M.A., F.L.S., V.M.H.

Introductory Note

None would dispute that the life's work of my husband was first and foremost plant-hunting. Nearly every large garden in the land bears witness to that work, for the riches of Asia which he brought to these islands are to be seen everywhere.

Nevertheless plant-hunting was not his sole occupation, for he was keenly observant, and had an extraordinary faculty for storing away odd scraps of apparently unrelated information, and then, possibly after many years, assembling them into an orderly pattern and drawing conclusions from the evidence. Such conclusions were sometimes startling, always stimulating, and for sheer excitement of the intellect his summings up often read more like the final chapter of a thriller than a sober scientific 'paper.'

Like most of us who have ever been fortunate enough to live among the hill tribes of Asia, my husband had their welfare very much at heart, as the following monograph clearly shows. It is to be hoped that the suggestions he offers will be put into action forthwith and 'carefully considered' *later*, as time permits.

J. K.-W.

THE phrase 'standard of living' is often loosely used. For my purpose I intend to define it as the lowest common denominator of food, goods, and well-being for any given nation or people—what everybody, even the poorest, does in fact possess or have access to. Different social and professional groups within a nation obviously have different living standards; we are here primarily concerned with the lowest—though it should always be borne in mind that a lowering of standards at the higher levels does not necessarily or always, or for long, improve those at the lower.

Environment determines what the basic standard is in a particular country. Adequate food, sufficient clothing, shelter—all these mean very different things to the Dyak and the Eskimo, and there are similar differences within South-east Asia itself. What the Kachin highlander of Burma or the Yunnanese peasant would consider adequate food, the Malay fisherman would not; while by western medical standards the diets of both are deficient. By their own empirical knowledge, even the most primitive tribes recognize the necessity for vitamins in their food; thus the Kachin makes journeys deep into his mountains in search of wild onions or bamboo shoots; the farmer of Yunnan germinates his beans before cooking them; and the wild Mishmi tribesman of the Assam frontier goes so far as to collect the stinking bugs (perhaps a relation of the French *punaises des bois*) from under stones in the dry river-beds in bamboo tubes, with which to season his rice or millet. But the supply even of these primitive but essential aids to health is inadequate, and a disproportionate amount of time is spent in collecting them.

Living standards anywhere, but especially in the under-developed countries, can only be raised gradually, and by increased production *all round*, not just in one single direction or one particular industry. Any exploitation of natural resources, whether mineral wealth, forest produce (timber and medicinal herbs), or introduced plants such as rubber and tea, does presently increase the wealth and so improve the diet and living conditions of the local population. This is not merely a matter of production, however, but of communications— to get the product out, to bring goods in, and to distribute them. It is at this point that the geographical approach is likely to be most fruitful.

For example, though the general prosperity of the Malay peninsula is due to the production of tin and of plantation rubber (introduced from Brazil by that great benefactor of South-east Asia, Sir Henry Wickham) the local benefits of this prosperity are due to the enterprise of the Chinese middlemen who have carried the consumer goods, for which the new wealth created a demand, into the remotest villages.

But without a road and rail system this comprehensive distribution would be impossible. Now, owing to the configuration of the country, communications are much easier in a north–south than in an east–west direction. Hence Malayan prosperity tends to run in parallel strips, and is most pronounced along the sea-board, where small coast-wise shipping still further increases the facilities for distribution. In the interior this well-being is less apparent, except where three or four navigable rivers running east or west create small centres where better living conditions prevail.

Another example of the importance of the geographical factor is furnished by North Burma. Here the physiography of the region is similar to that of the Malay peninsula in this: that the strike of the mountain ranges is north–south, though here the rivers flow southward between them. Here too, obviously, communications from south to north are much simpler than those *across* the grain of the country; but in Burma these obstacles are far more numerous and formidable than in Malaya; the mountain passes are blocked with snow for several months in the year, and when they are open the rivers are so swollen with rain and melting snow as to be extremely dangerous to cross. Hence for centuries North Burma (*i.e.*, the modern Kachin State north of the 26th parallel) was virtually cut off from central Burma for lack of communications.

Before the Second World War the British–Burma Government, who had only administered North Burma in the present century, at last took action and remedied this defect by cutting a road northward from Myitkyina to Putao. Till this was done, all imported goods for the Kachin tribes, including such essentials as salt, needles, cotton yarn, and cloth, had to be carried on men's backs, westward from China by Yunnanese and Lisu coolies. The effort required for even this relatively small lift can be gauged from the fact that, starting from the upper Mekong valley, they had to cross the Mekong–Salween divide by passes of thirteen thousand to fourteen thousand feet, then to negotiate the Salween River, climb the Salween–Irrawaddy divide beyond it by passes of twelve thousand to thirteen thousand feet, and descend to the formidable Taron River, where crossing could only be accomplished by difficult cane-rope bridges— since the swift current and many rapids make dug-out canoes much too dangerous—till, continuing westward and south-westward over innumerable lower ranges and small rivers, they reached Hkamti Long, in the heart of the Kachin country. (Indeed, Chinese pedlars were to be met with right up on the borders of Tibet at the source of the Adung River.) Nor did these people return to the Mekong valley empty-handed; they took back with them jungle produce— animal skins (such as bear, monkey, squirrel, and gooral), gold-dust, and medicines like Fritillaria bulbs and above all *teeta* (*Coptis teeta*, a close relation of the buttercup), the roots of which are in great demand as a febrifuge and tonic.

So much for the question of communications; these two examples may suffice to illustrate its relation to the main problem: the raising of living standards. To begin with these need to be raised in terms of 'things that you can touch and see'—food, clothing, housing, and household goods. After this should come education and medical and hospital services—for you cannot educate a hungry child, or a sick one. Ultimately, of course, there will remain to be dealt with the problem of the enjoyment of leisure ; but here we must take care not to make false comparisons between the Asiatic peasant and industrialized worker of the west. The aim must be to make life more worth living for the millions of human beings for whom, at present, it means chiefly drudgery, anxiety, and sickness, if not sheer want. Want, of course, is almost always more acute among town-dwellers than among country people, who have normally at least the resource of a plot of land—though to this generalization the peasant population of India is a lamentable exception.

Most of the hill tribes of Assam, Burma, Thailand, and Indo-China in fact have their own rather impressive and delightful ways of enjoying their periodic ceremonial binges, vaguely religious in origin, concerned chiefly with the village crops, and always involving a great deal of eating, drinking, and dancing. But life on the whole is hard and short, especially for the women.

Clearly it is as true of agricultural populations as it is of industrial ones that a higher standard of living must be preceded by greater output ; hence the chief requirement for the Asiatic peoples we are considering must be primarily food production, coupled with better communications by which to distribute it, and to export the forest produce which could be most fully exploited. For the hill peoples, at any rate, agriculture must always remain at the best near subsistence level ; and even this can only be assured by a better use of the land. All these possibilities come within the province of the geographer, who could make an overall survey, and prepare a land-utilization map. For, however small the scale of such a map at present, it could throw much light on the possible development of the region as a whole ; in fact, any balanced development is really impossible without such a survey. Planning is not a monopoly of the towns.

The monsoon region of South-east Asia lies mainly east of the 80th meridian and south of the 30th parallel. Confining ourselves to the mainland, this vast area consists of a lofty plateau in successive stages of erosion, extending from western Tibet to western China, and continued over the entire quadrant from due east to due south, by mountain ranges which overrun the escarpment and diverge like the outspread fingers of a hand. The general slope of the plateau is southward and eastward towards the coast. This is emphasized by the mountain ranges just referred to, which trend massively eastward, south-eastward, and southward.

The excessive erosion in this quadrant of Asia is due partly to the very heavy precipitation of the seasonal moisture-laden winds from the Indian Ocean—an annual rainfall of two hundred inches is not at all uncommon, while at Cherrapunjee, in Assam, it reaches six hundred inches, and at Dening about three hundred inches—and partly to the heavy glaciation which this part of Asia underwent during the Pleistocene period. Another important factor is a major line of weakness in the earth's crust running right through the region, which results in frequent and severe earthquakes. As these are not very destructive of human life, their effects are hardly noticed in the west.

Nearer the coast only two considerable plains, isolated from one another, survive—the Assam–Bengal plain in the north-west, and the Siam–Cambodia plain in the south-east. To these must be added the small but important deltas of the Irrawaddy and the Menam, lying between the two great plains, and that of the Red River beyond the Cambodian plain; five 'granaries' in all. (The greatest plain of South-east Asia, that which in pre-glacial times joined the Indonesian Islands with one another and with the mainland, now lies beneath the sea.)

Of the seven great rivers which drain this huge area, and are responsible for the fertility and irrigation of the plains—namely, from west to east, the Ganges, the Brahmaputra, the Irrawaddy, the Salween, the Mekong, the Red River, and the Yangtze—all except the Salween form deltas which are thickly populated. Owing, however, to climatic causes and the nature of the hinterland, with the exception of the Yangtze they are very unsatisfactory from the point of view of communications; though the Mekong holds possibilities of improvement in this respect.

Between the edge of the escarpment, whose outline has been blurred by severe erosion, and the plains, lie the foothills—an important sub-region. This thinly populated tract separates the plains, with their dense population, from the uninhabited mountains, as in turn the mountains separate the foothills from the much more populous plateau—foothills and mountains together are thus at once a link and a barrier between the plains and the plateau. This double zone is predominantly the zone of forest; and between the broad-leafed jungle below and the evergreen conifer forest above is wedged a narrow belt of semi-deciduous forest which is peculiarly rich in species of temperate trees. Above the conifer belt, at eleven thousand to twelve thousand feet, lies an alpine zone consisting of meadows and pastures, with bog in the valleys, and screes, bare rock outcrops, and cliffs on the intervening ridges. The passages through this highland labyrinth are neither numerous nor easy, and though most numerous at the eastern end, they are also more difficult to traverse there. This alpine zone can support cattle, sheep, and goats; but insecurity from the people of the plateau, and the difficulties in winter over food-stuffs in a region of such heavy snowfall, keep the numbers south of the escarpment to a minimum.

Judged, therefore, by vegetation cover, with its reaction on population density, the monsoon region of South-east Asia is seen on analysis to be made up of three sub-regions—namely (i) the plateau, deeply dissected round its edge; (ii) the axes of the main ranges as defined by their high peaks, with the foothills which lead up to them —the two together comprising the mountain zone; and (iii) the plains, where both population and living standards are highest. Plains contrast with plateau as agriculture contrasts with the pastoral life; they are the complements of one another, not rivals.

Minor sub-sub-regions are (a) the lower plateaux enclosed within the mountains (e.g., the Shan plateau and the Chin hills in Burma, the Khasi plateau in Assam, and the plateau of Traninh in Laos), (b) the river gorges of south-east Tibet, (c) the deltas of the principal rivers, and (d) the coastal mangrove swamps, so well developed on the west coast of Siam.

The proposed land utilization map would demarcate these areas for individual study and treatment, indicating their special suitability, if any, for residence, food production, industry, or development of natural resources such as forest products and minerals. Not less important are their communications with one another, a reminder that they must not be treated as though they were in watertight compartments.

The extreme irregularity of the coastline of South-east Asia may be contrasted with the striking regularity of that of Africa on the other side of the Indian Ocean. This is due to fundamental differences of structure, age of rocks, and history. Consider the deep gulfs and bays, the long peninsulas and narrow isthmuses, and the festoons of islands draping the shores of South-east Asia, with the straight sides of the immense Arabian block and of East Africa from Cape Gardafui to Mozambique. This fragmented coast line gives to Asia advantages which will immediately be appreciated. Not less advantageous for the purpose of communications is the dissection of the plateau edge, making the ascent from plains to plateau (once a way has been found) comparatively simple. Compare this with the abrupt unbroken walls of the Rift Valley, which may be regarded as the African equivalent. These intricate complications of the eastern scene ensure a number of micro-climates which in turn give rise to a corresponding variety of vegetation and flora. In fact, botanically, South-east Asia is one of the richest regions in the world—perhaps *the* richest. And considering the fundamental importance of plant life in the world's economy, the infinite possibilities of its position in that world should be kept in the foreground of any plans for development. There are probably no crops in the world which could not be grown in some corner of this region.

The population of South-east Asia, probably seventy-five per cent. of which is agricultural, is concentrated on the plains, deltas, and along the river valleys, where rice, easily irrigated, is the staple crop. This population is static. The few towns are situated mainly along the coast line, and are essentially seaports, looking out across the ocean rather than inland.

The population of the plateau is much smaller, and in fact partly nomadic, owing to the long distances the inhabitants must travel to find markets for their goods and to purchase necessities.

Communications between plateau and plains lie, as already pointed out, through the difficult intermediate zone of forested mountains. It is this intermediate zone which is the least known and hence the more worthy of study.

Nature cloaked the earth with a green mantle, which, though continually renewed, nevertheless gradually descends the scale from luxuriant tropical rain-forest to *tundra* with a minimum of plant life, and finally to lifeless naked desert, hot or frozen. This green mantle, with the animal kingdom and the minerals scattered through the earth's crust, the seas and the atmosphere, provide man with the raw materials of prosperity. But until he makes use of them they remain raw.

As the type of vegetation and its luxuriance depend on temperature, humidity, and light periodicity—which in turn depend on latitude, altitude, and topography—it is clear that man must treat the earth as he finds it.

At this point it will be helpful to emphasize the difference between the vegetation of a country (or region) and its flora. Vegetation refers solely to the *type* of natural cover—such as forest, scrub, grass, and so on—irrespective of its composition. The component elements of the vegetation type—that is to say, the actual plants found growing there—constitute its flora. The factors which control the flora are different from those which control the vegetation. Thus equatorial rain-forest is equatorial rain-forest whether it occurs on the Amazon, the Congo, or in Borneo. But a list of the species peculiar to rain-forest would be different in all three. Briefly, vegetation is general ; flora is particular.

The appearance of a region, thanks largely to its vegetation cover (or lack of it), gives a clue to its climate in general terms ; but only the flora, when known, can give an exact picture, though of a smaller part of the region. When we know what species grow in any particular area, we have at least a hint of what *might* grow there. It was of course a careful study of the floras of Ceylon and Malaya which enabled botanists to say, about the end of last century, that the Para rubber-plants raised from seed in the tropical house at Kew would probably do well there. The young plants were first sent out to Ceylon, and grown on at Heneratgoda, about twenty miles from Colombo, where several of them are still growing. As a result, rubber planting on a large scale was begun in both Ceylon and Malaya, thus starting a vast industry to match the vast motor industry which was growing up in the west. One has only to look at the large number of tropical South American medicinal and food plants —not to mention ornamental trees—which are grown in tropical Asia (*e.g.*, cocoa, tobacco, and quinine) to realize the possibilities.

But here again economic success is not a problem of production only—what to grow where—but also of available labour and transport. The most promising region of increased food production in South-east Asia is the great forest belt between the plains and the plateau, but this is precisely where the transport problem is most acute. High priority must be given to increasing the food supply, since the population, which continues to increase, should not only be fed, but *adequately* fed. A well-nourished community can more easily resist the debilitating diseases, such as malaria, yellow fever, or yaws, common in tropical countries. At the same time the effort to banish entirely these scourges (as yellow fever has been banished from the Panama Canal zone, and from parts of tropical west Africa, and malaria from parts of Assam) should of course continue.

The first step towards the profitable exploitation of the evergreen forest zone is its conservation. For very many years it has suffered from the ruinous destruction caused by blind felling and burning for an annual food crop, without any thought of the future. The results, as in North Burma, for example (the region best known to me) have been catastrophic. Tens of thousands of acres of good agricultural land for certain crops have been rendered for ever sterile, by the removal of all soil and the replacement of possibly valuable timber by useless grasses (particularly Saccharum and Imperata). It has resulted also in a perpetual threat of disastrous floods in the valleys, which in some parts have actually occurred. The *only* way to stop this wholesale slaughter of land capital is to control felling and introduce permanent cultivation by terracing.

In Yunnan and in Ceylon, as well as in parts of Assam (*e.g.*, the Naga hills and Manipur), slopes of thirty degrees to forty degrees are regularly terraced, and it is certain that any slope which is not too steep to be cultivated by the old destructive method could just as easily be terrace-cultivated.

The principal difficulty in North Burma consists less in the steepness of the foothills themselves than in the smallness of the villages and their distance from one another, which makes it difficult to concentrate man-power. The introduction of a small machine on the lines of a motor lawn-mower, for cutting out terraces on a slope, should not be beyond the ingenuity of engineers engaged in the manufacture of agricultural machinery.

The benefits to be derived from permanent terracing in place of temporary clearings are many, beginning with the substitution of wet rice for dry hill rice. It might be argued that at best this would do nothing to increase the food supply; all it would do—apart from conserving the forest—would be to economize labour. That is not so. Wet rice has a greater nutritional value than hill rice ; moreover, improved strains of irrigated rice are available which ripen at higher altitude, or in a shorter time, and these could be introduced. A more certain food supply in the hills would go far to check a rapidly increasing evil: the movement of the foothill population to the plains, whence they drift inevitably to the towns. This tendency has no single cause, but is a complicated long-term event. Leaving aside the fact that there are probably parts of the hills region which are really not fit for human habitation at all (e.g., the Mishmi hills, in Assam), there is a constant drift of peoples (notably of the Lisu tribe) westward from Yunnan and Szechwan into the Irrawaddy basin, which has been going on for at least half a century and probably much longer. This irregular migration in one direction sets up population pressures, shortage of land, and consequently of food, and so leads to further migrations. Thus there is a constant influx of hill-tribes into towns like Myitkyina and Bhamo, in North Burma, and Dibrugarh, in Assam. The former, in the course of less than twenty years, has changed from a large scattered village to a congested bustling town, with new slums. This is a disservice to both town and country. Indeed, one of the dangers in an abrupt rise in living standards for a certain number of the town-dwellers is that it attracts population. Even if there are some opportunities for the newcomer to reach the higher standard (which is doubtful), it is certain that very few will in fact reach it, since the only *certain* employment in the towns is coolie labour ; hence the majority will be worse off than they were at home.

It is important, therefore, to improve the hill villages *as villages*, and not try to turn them into something else, alien to the inhabitants ; to do that would be no better than to leave them stagnant, though it is precisely this stagnation which is so destructive of their best qualities. For generations, all who can be spared from the village during the winter months, when there is no agricultural work in the hills, have been accustomed to go down to the plains as labourers. Here they find temporary work on the roads or on the railway, cutting cane and firewood, manning ferry-boats, and so on, thereby earning a little money with which to purchase a few luxuries and keep themselves without drawing on the village supplies. Most of these seasonal workers return to their villages at the beginning of the hot weather (March-April). But of late years, owing partly to the slow decay of village life, and partly to the meretricious attractions of life in towns like Myitkyina, more and more young men have tended to stay away from their homes altogether.

Governments, then, cannot afford to neglect the hill villages, and should do everything possible to make village life more attractive and worth while. For instance, piped water to different points in the village would do much to ease the lot of the overworked hill women. (The abundance of bamboo should ensure, almost everywhere, that the laying of such pipes placed no burden upon meagre economic resources.) Most villages too, even those of the wild and primitive Mishmis, own cattle; however, these are kept for ceremonial sacrifice only and are never milked, and the children are thus deprived of a valuable addition to their deficient diet. Inquiry reveals no religious prejudice against the milking of cattle—only ignorance of the art and lack of enterprise to experiment. Again, some attempt at sanitation would surely improve the standard of health all round. At present there is usually none, not even so much as the simplest earth closet. Gardening should be taught and encouraged, to ensure a greater variety of fruit and vegetables; while a little system in the manner of raising poultry should soon bring about a satisfactory increase in the size of the hen and her egg.

All these improvements would demand a supply of trained, patient, and tactful instructors, not without a spirit of dedication to their task. After all that would come the building of a central hospital with numerous satellite dispensaries in the different villages round about. It is fashionable for Governments (with their eye always on the next general election) to attract votes by the building of village schools. However, a little reflection might reveal the fact that from the hill *villagers'* point of view, academic education should be the final aim, not the initial one. At present the type of education offered makes only for discontent and helps to send young people off to the towns, where there are no jobs for them yet. There, as often as not, they get into bad company, and a new series of problems is born.

I have sometimes been struck by the excellence of the school buildings and the eagerness of the children in the hills, but appalled by the ignorance and indifference of the teachers. The appointment of suitable teachers is often a difficult and delicate matter, but it is of vital importance that they should be interested in their job, and preferably belong to the same tribe as the pupils.

The pioneers of education in the hills were the European and American missionaries, the majority of whom did excellent work.

Unfortunately, there was sometimes inter-denominational rivalry, which left its mark on the tribes, who occasionally carry on the petty jealousies of rival missions long since departed. Hence the greatest obstacle to raising living standards in the hills is not lack of money, but lack of co-operation. Human inertia is an irresistible force, particularly when allied with peasant conservatism; and opposition to the introduction of revolutionary practices—especially in so fundamental an occupation as agriculture—is likely to be formidable.

The forest belt contains not only timber but valuable medicinal herbs also. The flora is, however, so little known that it seems inappropriate to discuss these possibilities at this stage, though it is worth pointing out that the exploitation of minor forest produce (cane, bamboos, medicinal herbs) is comparatively easy, since it involves no insuperable difficulties of transport. It is these difficulties which make the extraction of timber, and mining of minerals, almost prohibitive at present. So far the only solution for the extraction of timber which suggests itself is to take it out in the form of sawn planks. The Chinese take out planks of Taiwania, the coffin-tree, at Htawgaw—the trees are felled in the forest, sawn into thick planks on the spot, and shaped as required for the particular purpose with an adze. The coffin planks can be floated down rivers like the Ngawchaung, which are too shallow to float logs, and stored at a base. After being seasoned they are carried over the mountain passes on the backs of men and mules into China. Although this is a specialized industry, there is no reason why other timbers for which special uses can be found should not be extracted in the same way. It would be worth while to survey some of North Burma's many rivers with a view to floating planks, if only for short distances, down from the hills. In the low-water season (*i.e.*, in winter) few of even the secondary rivers will float logs.

Forest officers are inclined to dismiss the trees of these inaccessible forests as useless, on far too little evidence, or none. They are familiar with about a dozen widespread timber-trees, such as teak (Tectona), Xylia, Terminalia, padouk, and so forth; anything besides these is regarded with indifference. Until we know much more about the species in the forests of North Burma than we do at present, this is a very mistaken attitude.

North Burma is so blanketed by forest that little has been done about its mineral wealth, if any. Small galena deposits have long been known to the hill tribes, and both the lead and the silver are extracted by reduction on primitive hearths, the lead for bullets, the silver for ornaments. But it is useless at present to attempt the exploitation of anything but the most valuable minerals. Much money was wasted by the Mines Department not long ago in an attempt to exploit a galena deposit, though it should have been obvious from the start that the cost of transport would far exceed the worth of the product. Possibly the idea behind the venture was that uranium also might be found. But the new techniques of magnetic prospecting from the air should prevent such mistakes in future. Gold dust also has long been known to occur in some riverbeds, and is collected, much of it doubtless finding its way into China. Gold, however, has not been found in paying quantities.

A potential asset in North Burma is water power. Though almost unlimited, it is not readily harnessed because there are comparatively few vertical falls. However, there is at least one useful one on the Taron River.

It might, however, be possible—and certainly less expensive—to establish a small power station much closer to Myitkyina than that —e.g., at the Irrawaddy confluence, about twenty-six miles distant. This could produce enough power to drive small machines, besides providing electric light—as in fact is done in the Naga hills of Assam. (Myitkyina already has an electric-light plant, privately owned.) Power is essential to any modern community, even for very minor industries. (The success of the Chinese in developing small industries in Singapore, Hongkong, and other places on the coast shows what can be done under favourable conditions of population and transport.) The hill tribes have long made use of crude wooden machines, driven by water power, to save labour, and saw-mills so driven could be established at small cost.

Although there is little likelihood of industry penetrating into the evergreen forest belt of North Burma in the foreseeable future, if ever, it is nevertheless essential that steps be taken immediately to curb the destruction of the forests. At present most of the forest above about seven thousand feet is relatively safe, since that is the upper limit of cultivation. But there is a growing tendency to destroy it by fire alone at much higher altitudes than that, wherever there is a sufficiently long dry season, in the interests of the game hunters— e.g., in the Adung valley and on Mount Victoria in the Chin hills, where the annual grass fires destroy the forest little by little up to ten thousand feet. It is almost impossible to ensure that forest and game laws are observed in such remote regions; probably nature reserves and national parks offer the best prospects of saving the forest, and with it all animal life, from extinction. A greater area of Burma is under forest than under cultivation, chiefly because the mountain area is much greater than that of the plains; but more than half the forest is classed as inaccessible, and many forest

The white flowers of Rhododendron bullatum, flushed with pink and heavy with fragrance, are one of the rewards of the plant hunter when he reaches 8000 ft. in the mountains of North Burma and Assam

A tree rhododendron in its prime, Tibet

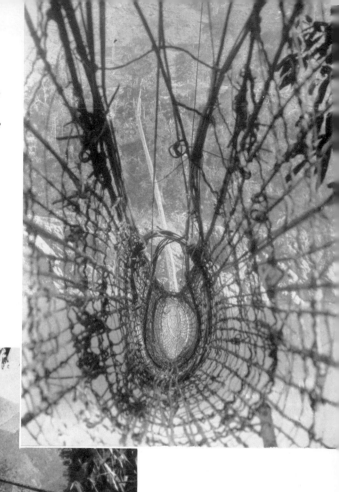

Such bridges as these, in the Abor hills, Assam, made entirely of cane and bamboo, do much to enliven a weary march. The 'spider's web' (Right) is over 600 ft. long

177

officers believe that it will always remain so. Even if that proves true its conservation is still most important. If the forest is finally destroyed irreparable damage will be done on the plains, not only to the agricultural lands, but also to communications; and as to the foothills themselves, agriculture would have to be abandoned altogether, thereby destroying the entire local economy.

There are several reasons for this: first, the direct loss of timber, even if much of it is at present commercially useless, would be serious. Again, the rapid loss of good soil, and the deep gullying which would follow, would quickly render the steep slopes quite barren, as can be observed anywhere in the hills. Secondary effects are the damming of streams with consequent danger of flooding, the lowering of the water table, and minor alterations of climate. With loss of soil and fertility, only the coarsest and most useless plants will grow, and once established, they are almost impossible to eradicate, but continue to spread like wildfire. The damage is cumulative and far-reaching. As a result of reckless burning on the slopes, and the consequent flooding, I have seen forest in the valley bottoms drowned where it stands.

Here and there in the hills one comes across experiments in terracing which have been abandoned, either because of labour shortage, or because this novel method did not give the hoped-for results immediately—or simply because the old methods were preferred. In Burma, as elsewhere, inertia is probably the greatest obstacle to progress still to be overcome. Yet progress in this sense is the only possible solution to the problem of food and population.

The introduction of new crops is a long-term project, but what it can ultimately achieve is well illustrated by the success of the tea industry in Assam, which (economically at least) has been far more valuable to the people of the province than the same area of rice could have been. Nor has the land used for tea been taken, for the most part, from rice land, though much of it was originally forest, whose frontiers are inexorably being pushed back; much of it also was useless swamp land—useless until drained, that is, but good soil nevertheless.

That the dwindling forest resources of South-east Asia are not being fully utilized is clear enough; but there is no single reason for this, and certainly no one cure. Many of the best forest regions are, as has already been explained, still inaccessible and may always remain so. But there are bottle-necks at the export end, as well as difficulties in the forests themselves. Shipping, for example, is woefully short, and Burma is unable to keep up her export quota of even so saleable a timber as teak, for lack of ships; logs pile up in Rangoon and deteriorate. Until this immediate bottle-neck is removed, it may seem unrealistic to urge more detailed exploration of the inaccessible forests; however, it is necessary to know as much as possible about these regions, and how best to make use of anything valuable which more intensive exploration may reveal. The first necessity is therefore a botanical survey to ascertain not only what species exist, but where the chief concentrations of particular species are; their incidence may be very uneven.

So far as the actual species are concerned, the foundation of forestry is botany. Botanic gardens, herbaria, and research institutions are essential tools for the exploration and utilization of forests; the correct identification of species is a strict necessity. But with the material and literature so widely scattered as it is to-day, and the changing modern nomenclature of species, this becomes ever more difficult. The amount of time, money, and human effort wasted because of wrong identifications, or because people are really discussing two different plants, is almost incredible. However, to-day the time and expense involved in building up a modern research centre has made such an enterprise a rather remote possibility, although, of course, in India (*e.g.*, Dehra Dun, Calcutta Botanic Garden, and many other places), Singapore, Java (Buitenzorg—modern Bogor—was the finest tropical botanic garden in the world), and elsewhere, such research stations have long existed, but need to be kept up to date. Recourse must therefore be had to other means. It is suggested that a botanist from each country of South-east Asia might be attached to one or other of the botanical institutions in Europe, where he would have access to the collections of Asiatic plants and their literature, and then act as liaison between the European pool of knowledge and his own Government institution, while working on the materials for a Flora. The ideal to be aimed at would of course be a Flora for each sovereign State, or at least regional Floras. (There would have to be several of these for Burma alone.) While there exist for India a number of good regional Floras (none of them very modern, however), and a comprehensive, though still less up-to-date, Flora of India, there is very little of the sort in existence for the other countries of South-east Asia. Ceylon and Malaya have their Floras—the former far from up to date—and the magnificent *Flora Malesiana* is appearing periodically. But much remains to be done elsewhere, especially in the realm of local Floras which could be used in schools. For unless interest can be aroused in the young, the required number of biologists in general, and of botanists in particular, to study and make use of the rich tropical vegetation will never be forthcoming.

A large part of the population of South-east Asia is brought up in an environment conditioned by the vegetation. Thus they come to take this for granted, as part of the natural order of things. The forest is either their whole life, as peasants and food-gatherers, or it is nothing. It does not 'lead to a job.'

It is this growing anxiety, or perhaps necessity, for a 'job' which draws so many young persons from the hills to the towns, and helps to increase the congestion there. Meanwhile the hills tend to become depopulated while the problems of that region are ignored or forgotten. On the plains it is the growing lawlessness which drives the population—often dispossessed—to the comparative security of the towns, where they become squatters.

Indeed, it is not possible to keep the problems of South-east Asia entirely free of politics, which of course they should be.

Thus there are three possibilities for the maintenance and exploitation (in the best sense of the word) of the mountain forest region, which means primarily the foothills and lesser ranges:

(i) The extraction of natural vegetable products—timber, medicinal herbs, horticultural plants, and of such substances as resins, tannins, shellac, oils, and many other substances. This is not a very promising field at present, except on a small scale, but the possibilities should be borne in mind.

(ii) The discovery of minerals, which at the moment holds out even less promise than (i). Unless the mineral is a really valuable one—platinum, uranium, or possibly gold or oil—it has no immediate usefulness for reasons already given. In any case, mineral wealth is a wasting asset, whereas vegetable wealth is self-reproducing, and if properly managed gives a continuous and inexhaustible yield. The same is true of animal wealth.

(iii) As areas for the introduction of new crops—the most profitable line to follow up at the moment. There is room for wide-reaching experiment here, but expensive mistakes, such as happened in Africa with the Groundnut Scheme (easily avoidable if expert advice had been sought and taken) must at all costs be avoided. At the beginning of this century the cultivation of tea at Kanpetlct, in Burma, was attempted, but was apparently not a success, although Tea Camellias grow on Mount Victoria, and tea is successfully grown in the Shan States. Several alien crops for which there is a demand have been tried on the Shan plateau, with fair success; but they do not seem to have been proceeded with diligently. There is room for further experiment here, and in other parts of Burma also. The cultivation of Citrus fruits suggests itself in certain places, such as the dry zone of Burma, the coast of Annam, and elsewhere. There are further possibilities, with lychees, groundnuts, saffron, cloves, horticultural products, including orchids, and other things.

The agricultural East has one asset which the industrial West lacks—an almost limitless supply of cheap labour which is landless and comparatively fluid. It is largely concentrated in the cities (where it helps to lower the standard of living), having been drawn there by the search for work.

To sum up the overall physical aspect of South-east Asia, common in varying degrees to western India, Burma, Assam, Malaya, Siam (Thailand), Yunnan, and Indo-China: there are plains lining a great river valley which ends in a delta (sometimes in an estuary), the neighbouring coast being fringed with mangrove swamp. The river valleys are invested by mountains composed of parallel ranges, stepped up rather abruptly to a plateau, which is often so deeply dissected as no longer to resemble even remotely a plateau, though its structure suggests that it began as one.

The mountains are arranged in three groups, the main central ranges, and the inner and outer ranges, the latter being the foothills.

The principal river is usually, but not always, navigable for some distance, and the big towns are usually either seaports or riverine ports. The plateaux, foothills, plains (including the river valleys), and deltas are inhabited in varying degrees, the plateaux and foothills being the least, the plains and deltas the most, thickly populated. Over most of the enormous area a tropical climate with abundant though seasonal rainfall prevails, the alluvial and forest soils are everywhere rich, and water is adequate. Almost anything will grow under such conditions.

This is the general outline picture we have to keep in mind when planning for the future of South-east Asia.

A List of Publications of F. Kingdon-Ward

Compiled by W. T. STEARN

Contributions to Periodicals

1911a. Letter from China. *Gard. Chron.* III. **50**: 292.
1911b. Plant collecting in the Chinese Alps. *Gard. Chron.* III. **50**: 458–459.
1912a. Some plant formations from the arid regions of western China. *Ann. Bot.* **26**: 1105–1110.
1912b. Plant-collecting in Yunnan. *Gard. Chron.* III. **52**: 1–2.
1912c. Through the Lutzu country to Menkong. *Geogr. J. (London)*, **39**: 582–592.
1912d. Mistleto in Shensi. *Gard. Chron.* III. **52**: 147–148.
1912e. Journeys by the River of Golden Sand. *Gard. Chron.* III. **52**: 325–326.
1912f. On the altitudinal limits of plants in north-west Yunnan. *New Phytol.* **11**: 333–346.
1913a. Plant collecting in China. *Gard. Chron.* III. **53**: 129–130, 418–419.
1913b. Wanderings of a naturalist in Tibet and western China. *Scottish Geogr. Mag.* **29**: 341–350.
1916a. Notes on the flora of the W. Ssŭch'uan mountains. *N. China Branch Roy. Asiat. Soc.*, new ser. **47**: 39–48.
1916b. Some plant associations of N.W. Yunnan. *Trans. Bot. Soc. Edinburgh*, **27**: 1–13.
1916c. On the Sino-Himalayan flora. *Trans. Bot. Soc. Edinburgh*, **27**: 13–53.
1916d. Notes on a journey across Tsa-rung. *Geogr. J. (London)*, **47**: 45–51.
1916e. Glacial phenomena on the Yunnan-Tibet frontier. *Geogr. J. (London)*, **48**: 55–68.
1918. The hydrography of the Yunnan-Tibet frontier. *Geogr. J. (London)*, **52**: 288–299.
1919. On the possible prolongation of the Himalayan axis beyond the Dihang. *Geogr. J. (London)*, **54**: 231–241.
1920a. The valleys of Kham. *Geogr. J. (London)*, **56**: 183–195.
1920b. Alpine meadows of Burma-Yunnan. *Gard. Chron.* III. **67**: 118.
1920c. Plant collecting on Imaw Bum. *Gard. Chron.* III. **67**: 168, 228–229, 306–307.
1920d. The pass of the winds and waters. *Gard. Chron.* III. **68**: 240, 310.
1920e. Rhododendrons on the N.E. frontier of Burma. *The Garden*, **84**, 194–196.
1920f. Primulas on the north-east frontier of Burma. *The Garden*, **84**: 322, 489–490, 500.
1921a. Shrubs on the north-east frontier of Burma. *Gard. Chron.* III. **69**: 42.
1921b. Scree plants. *Gard. Chron.* III. **69**: 78.

1921c. The botanical exploration of the north-east frontier. *Gard. Chron.* III. **69**: 114–115.

1921d. The Mekong-Salween divide as a geographical barrier. *Geogr. J.* (*London*), **58**: 49–56, map.

1921e. The distribution of floras in S.E. Asia as affected by the Burma-Yunnan ranges. *J. Indian Bot.* **2**: 20–26, map.

1921f. Reginald Farrer. *Geogr. J.* (*London*), **57**: 69–70.

1921g. On the road to Htagaw. *Gard. Chron.* III. **69**: 186.

1921–22. Mr Kingdon Ward's sixth expedition in Asia. *Gard. Chron.* III. **69**: 234, 298 (1921); **70**: 48, 100, 124, 184, 220 (1921); **71**: 6, 30, 115–116, 138–139, 166, 196–197, 229–230, 260, 290–291, 321–322 (1922); **72**: 6–7, 34, 52–53, 80, 122, 150–151, 178–179, 208, 238 (1922).

1922. The glaciation of Chinese Tibet. *Geogr. J.* (*London*), **59**: 363–369.

1922–23. Mr Kingdon Ward's seventh expedition in Asia. *Gard. Chron.* III. **72**: 268, 296–297, 325, 352, 378–379 (1922); **73**: 22, 50, 80, 107, 134, 162, 186–187, 214, 246, 300–301, 350–351 (1923); **74**: 6, 40, 102, 130–131, 188–189, 234, 262, 294, 378 (1923).

1923a. The flora of the Tibetan Marches. *J. R. Hort. Soc.* (*London*), **48**: 201–212.

1923b. From the Yangtse to the Irrawaddy. *Geogr. J.* (*London*), **60**: 6–20.

1924a. The snow mountains of Yunnan. *Geogr. J.* (*London*), **64**: 222–231.

1924b. Rhododendrons. *Gard. Chron.* III. **75**: 222, 240, 256–257, 306, 358–359; **76**: 12, 24–25, 46, 62–63, 116, 124–125, 199–200, 236–237, 253, 264, 286, 304, 320–321, 332–333, 356.

1924–26. Mr F. Kingdon Ward's eighth expedition in Asia. *Gard. Chron.* III. **75**: 206–207, 288–289, 381–382 (1924); **76**: 97–98, 148, 214–215, 300–301 (1924); **77**: 236–237, 318–330, 394–395, 434–436 (1925); **78**: 12–13, 50–52, 90–91, 130–131, 191–192, 230–231, 292–293, 330–331, 408–409, 448–449, 482–483 (1925); **79**: 8–9, 47–48, 118–119, 151–152, 190–191, 232–233 (1926).

1925a. Some Tibetan primulas. *The Garden*, **89**: 445–447.

1925b. Some Nivalis primulas from Tibet. *The Garden*, **89**: 713–714.

1925c. Address by Captain Kingdon Ward. *Rhodod. Soc. Notes*, **3**: 5–15.

1926a. Notes on the genus Meconopsis, with some additional species from Tibet. *Ann. Bot.* **40**: 535–546.

1926b. The genus Meconopsis. *Gard. Chron.* III. **79**: 252–253, 306–308, 340, 438–439, 459–460.

1926c. The blue poppies. *The Garden*, **90**: 96–97, 115–116.

1926d. Some Tibetan primulas. *The Garden*, **90**: 313–314.

1926e. Explorations in south-eastern Tibet. *Geogr. J.* (*London*), **67**: 97–123.

1926f. Narrative and observations on distribution. *Notes R. Bot. Gard. Edinburgh*, **15**: 89–97.

1926–28. Mr F. Kingdon Ward's ninth expedition in Asia. *Gard. Chron.* III. **80**: 130, 170–171, 290–291, 410–411 (1926); **81**: 10–11, 130–131, 162–163, 194–195, 250–251, 303–304, 394–396, 432–434 (1927); **82**: 90–91, 150–152, 210–211, 268–269, 309–310, 366–367, 406–407, 446–447, 486–487, 522–523 (1927); **83**: 28–29, 64–65, 102–103, 138–139 (1928).

1927a. Tibetan primulas of the Sikkimensis section. *Gard. Chron.* III. **82**: 172–174.

1927b. The blue poppies. *Gardening Illustrated.* **49**: 608–609.
1927c. Botanical explorations in Tibet. *J. R. Hort. Soc. (London),* **52**: 15–24, 225–234.
1927d. The Sino-Himalayan flora. *Proc. Linn. Soc. London,* **139**: 67–74.
1927e. A note on deglaciation in Tibet. *Geol. Mag.* **64**: 278–281.
1927f. Address by Captain Kingdon Ward. *Rhodod. Soc. Notes.* **3**: 145–150.
1928. Burmese species of Meconopsis. *Ann. Bot.* **42**: 855–862.
1929a. *Rhododendron repens* and its allies. *Gard. Chron.* III. **86**: 266–267.
1929b. Three new rhododendrons from Tibet. *Gard. Chron.* III. **86**: 503–504.
1929c. Botanical explorations in the Mishmi Hills. *Himal. J.* **1**: 51–59.
1929d. Botanical exploration: Mishmi Hills, Assam. *Proc. Linn. Soc. London,* **142**: 60–64.
1930a. The Sino-Himalayan node. *Abstr. Fifth Internat. Bot. Congr. Cambridge,* 322–324.
1930b. The distribution of primulas from the Himalaya to China, with descriptions of some new species. *Ann. Bot.* **44**: 111–125.
1930c. The forests of the north-east frontier of India. *Empire Forest. J.* **9**: 11–31, map.
1930d. *Primula Agleniana* and its allies. *Gard. Chron.* III. **87**: 12–13.
1930e. *Primula eucyclia.* W. W. Sm. et Forrest (K. W. 6, 822). *Gard. Chron.* III. **87**: 287.
1930f. Botanical exploration. *Gard. Chron.* III. **87**: 309–310.
1930g. Two Tibetan rhododendrons. *Gard. Chron.* III. **87**: 330.
1930h. Three Indo-Himalayan magnolias. *Gard. Chron.* III. **87**: 451–452.
1930j. Some woodland primulas. *Gard. Chron.* III. **88**: 8–9.
1930k. Notes on "candelabra" primulas. *Gard. Chron.* III. **88**: 70–71.
1930l. Giant sorrels [Rheum]. *Gard. Chron.* III. **88**: 134–135.
1930m. *Rhododendron patulum* and its allies. *Gard. Chron.* III. **88**: 298–299.
1930n. *Fritillaria flavida* Rendle and *Nomocharis nana* E. H. Wilson. *J. Bot. (London),* **68**: 120.
1930o. The Seinghku and Delei valleys, north-east frontier of India. *Geogr. J. (London),* **75**: 412–435.
1930p. Botanical exploration on the Burma-Tibet frontier. *Proc. Linn. Soc. London,* **144**: 140–143.
1932a. The mahogany "triflorum" Rhododendron. *Gard. Chron.* III. **91**: 396.
1932b. Plant hunting beyond Burma. *Gard. Chron.* III. **91**: 444–445.
1932c. *Primula dumicola* W. W. Sm. *Gard. Chron.* III. **92**: 59.
1932d. *Lilium hyacinthinum* Wilson. *R. Hort. Soc., Lily Year Book,* **1932**: 62–63.
1932e. Botanical explorations on the Burma-Tibet frontier. *Geogr. J. (London),* **80**: 465–483.
1932–33. Mr F. Kingdon Ward's eleventh expedition in Asia. *Gard. Chron.* III. **91**: 256–257, 292–293, 329–330, 365–366, 422–423, 462–463 (1932); **92**: 8–9, 42–43, 78–80, 118–119, 158–160, 194–195, 231–232, 266–267, 302–303, 388–389, 374–375, 428–429, 465–466 (1932); **93**: 8–9, 42–43, 81–82, 134–135, 170–171, 206–207, 242–243, 276–277, 314–315, 362–363, 402–403, 432–434 (1933); **94**: 26–27, 62–63, 98–99, 142–143, 180–181, 218–219, 254–255, 290–291, 326–327, 362–364, 400–401, 416–417, 454–455, 488 (1933).

1933a. *Rhododendron leucaspis. Gard. Chron.* III. **94**: 65–66.
1933b. Plant collecting at the source of the Irrawaddy. *J. R. Hort. Soc.* (*London*), **58**: 103–114.
1933c. A naturalist's journey to the sources of the Irrawaddy. *Himal. J.* **5**: 46–47.
1934a. Some new and rare gentians. *Gard. Chron.* III. **95**: 263–264.
1934b. Some good Labiatae. *Gard. Chron.* III. **95**: 326.
1934c. Hunting for rock plants in high Asia. *Gard. Chron.* III. **95**: 390–391.
1934d. Some observations on Tibetan lilies. *R. Hort. Soc., Lily Year Book,* **1934**: 46–49.
1934e. The Himalaya east of the Tsangpo. *Geogr. J.* (*London*), **84**: 369–397.
1934f. Explorations in Tibet, 1933. *Proc. Linn. Soc. London.* **146**: 110–113.
1934g. The Himalaya east of the Tsangpo. *Geogr. J.* (*London*), **84**: 369–397.
1935a. Rhododendron seeds, with special reference to their classification. *J. Bot.* (*London*), **73**: 241–247.
1935b. A sketch of the geography and botany of Tibet, being materials for a flora of that country. *J. Linn. Soc. Bot.* **50**: 239–265, maps.
1935c. The forest of Tibet. *Himal. J.* **7**: 101–116.
1936a. *Dracocephalum Hemsleyanum. Gard. Chron.* III. **100**: 176–177.
1936b. Botanical and geographical explorations in Tibet, 1935. *Geogr. J.* (*London*), **88**: 385–413, map.
1936c. Across southern Tibet. *J. R. Hort. Soc.* (*London*), **61**: 273–276.
1936d. Exploring for plants in southern Tibet. *Nature,* **137**: 750.
1936e. A sketch of the vegetation and geography of Tibet. *Proc. Linn. Soc. London,* **148**: 133–160, map.
1936f. Across southern Tibet. *Himal. J.* **8**: 124–129.
1936g. Botanical and geographical explorations in Tibet, 1935. *Geogr. J.* (*London*), **88**: 385–413.
1936–37. Mr Kingdon Ward's thirteenth expedition in Asia. *Gard. Chron.* III. **99**: 264–265, 296–297, 328–329, 370–371, 402–403 (1936); **100**: 268–269, 302–304, 336–337, 372–373, 408–409 (1936); **101**: 8–9, 40–41, 88–89, 120–121, 170–172, 206–207, 240–241, 290–291, 330–331, 364–365, 406–407, 440–441 (1937); **102**: 8–9, 62–63, 142–143, 178–179, 214–215, 252–253 (1937).
1938a. *Cotoneaster conspicua. Gard. Chron.* III. **103**: 267.
1938b. *Parochetus communis. Gard. Chron.* III. **104**: 406.
1938–39. Mr Kingdon Ward's fourteenth expedition in Asia. *Gard. Chron.* III. **103**: 252–253, 302, 336–337, 370–371, 412–413, 447–448 (1938); **104**: 26–27, 80–81, 120–122, 160–161, 196–197, 232–233, 268–269, 304–305, 338–339, 372–373, 404–405, 438–439, 474–475 (1938); **105**: 24–25, 72–73, 108–109, 166–167, 200–201, 248–249, 308–309, 350–351, 386–387 (1939); **106**: 8–9, 62–63, 98–99, 142–143, 194–195, 226–227 (1939).
1939a. The Irrawaddy plateau. *Geogr. J.* (*London*), **94**: 293–308.
1939b. Ka Karpo Razi: Burma's highest peak. *Himal. J.* **9**: 74–88.
1940a. Botanical and geographical exploration in the Assam Himalaya. *Geogr. J.* (*London*), **96**: 1–13.

1940b. Exploration in the Eastern Himalaya. *J. R. Central Asiatic Soc.* **27**: 211–220.

1941. The Vernay-Cutting Expedition, Nov. 1938 to April 1939. Report on the vegetation and flora of the Hpimaw and Htawgaw Hills, Northern Burma. *Brittonia*, **4**: 1–19.

1942. An outline of vegetation and flora of Tibet. *Roy. Bot. Gardens, Calcutta*, 150*th Anniv. Vol.*, 99–103.

1944–45. A sketch of the botany and geography of North Burma. *J. Bombay Nat. Hist. Soc.* **44**: 550–574 (1944); **45**: 16–30 (1944); **45**: 133–148 (1945).

1946a. Additional notes on the botany of North Burma. *J. Bombay Nat. Hist. Soc.* **46**: 381–390.

1946b. Botanical explorations in North Burma. *J. R. Hort. Soc. (London)*, **71**: 318–325.

1946c. A liliaceous plant from Manipur: lily or nomocharis? (K.W. 16008). *R. Hort. Soc., Lily Year Book*, **10**: 62–68.

1947. Tibet as a grazing land. *Geogr. J. (London)*, **110**: 60–76.

1948a. Rhododendrons in Burma, Assam, and Tibet. *R. Hort. Soc., Rhodod. Year Book*, **2** (for 1947): 13–20.

1948b. Observations on the classification of the genus Rhododendron. *R. Hort. Soc., Rhodod. Year Book*, **2** (for 1947): 99–114.

1948c. The Manipur Nomocharis. *Gard. Chron.* III. **124**: 84, 92.

1949a. Plant hunting in Manipur. *J. R. Hort. Soc. (London)*, **74**: 288–295, 334–340.

1949b. Rhododendrons in the wild. *R. Hort. Soc., Rhodod. Year Book*, **4** (for 1949): 9–19.

1951a. Notes on the Assam earthquake. *Nature*, **167**: 130–131.

1951b. The Assam Earthquake of 1950. Penguin *Science News*, No. 22.

1953. A new Burmese lily. *Gard. Chron.* III. **134**: 238.

1953b. The Lohit valley in 1950. *Proc. Linn. Soc. London*, **164**: 2–8.

1953c. The Assam earthquake of 1950. *Geogr. J. (London)*, **119**: 169–182.

1954a. More about the new Burmese lily. *Gard. Chron.* III. **135**: 144.

1954b. Progress of the Burmese lily. *Gard. Chron.* III. **136**: 66.

1954c. Lilies and allied plants found in Burma. *R. Hort. Soc., Lily Year Book*, **18**: 121–131.

1954d. Report on the forests of the North Triangle, Kachin State, North Burma. *J. Bombay Nat. Hist. Soc.* **52**: 304–320.

1955a. Aftermath of the great Assam earthquake of 1950. *Geogr. J. (London)*, **121**: 290–303.

1955b. Plant-hunting in the Triangle, North Burma. *J. R. Hort. Soc. (London)*, **80**: 174–190, maps.

1955c. Collectors' numbers; reasons for their retention. *R. Hort. Soc., Rhodod. & Camellia Year Book*, **10** (for 1956): 48–51.

1958a. Wie Rhododendron wächsen. *Rhodod. und immergrüne Laubgeh. Jahrb.* 1958: 7–13.

1958b. Collector's commentary. *The Rhododendron*, pp. 19–23. Editor, B. L. Urquhart.

1959. A sketch of the flora and vegetation of Mount Victoria in Burma. *Acta Horti Gotoburg.* **22**: 53–74.

Books

1913. *The Land of the Blue Poppy: Travels of a Naturalist in Eastern Tibet.*
1921. *In Farthest Burma.*
1923. *The Mystery Rivers of Tibet.*
1924. *From China to Hkamti Long.*
1924. *The Romance of Plant Hunting.*
1926. *The Riddle of the Tsangpo Gorges.*
1926. *Rhododendrons for Everyone.*
1930. *Plant Hunting on the Edge of the World.*
1931. *Plant Hunting in the Wilds.*
1932. *The Loom of the East.*
1934. *A Plant Hunter in Tibet.*
1935. *The Romance of Gardening.*
1937. *Plant Hunter's Paradise.*
1941. *Assam Adventure.*
1945. *Modern Exploration.*
1946. *About this Earth.*
1948. *Commonsense Rock Gardening.*
1949. *Rhododendrons and Azaleas.*
1949. *Burma's Icy Mountains.*
1950. *Footsteps in Civilization.*
1952. *Plant Hunter in Manipur.*
1954. *Berried Treasure.*
1956. *Return to the Irrawaddy.*

Kingdon-Ward's life was so nomadic—even in August 1947 he described himself in a guest-book as being "of no fixed abode"—that he accumulated hardly any possessions and kept no record or set of his publications. Hence the above list of contributions to periodicals, for which E. D. Merrill and E. H. Walker's *A Bibliography of Eastern Asiatic Botany*, 521–524 (1938) and U. Schweinfurth's *Die horizontale und vertikale Verbreitung der Vegetation im Himalaya (Bonner Geogr. Abhandl.* **20**): 360–362 (1957) provided the basis, is certainly incomplete.

Index

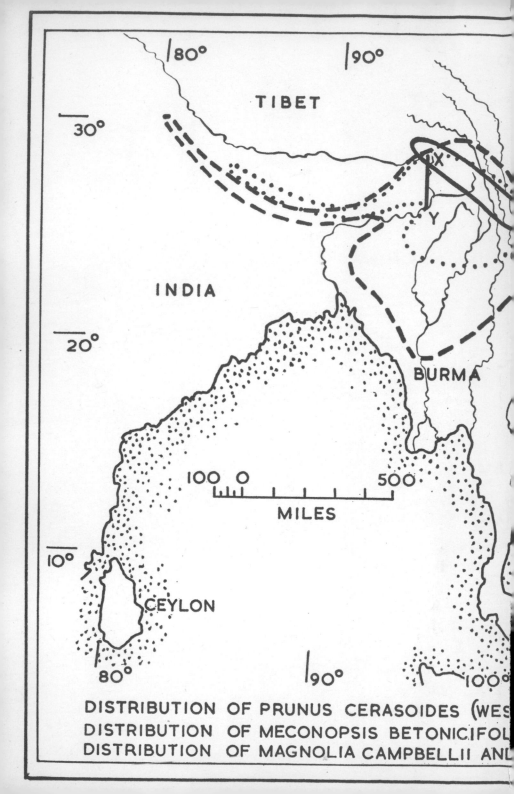

DISTRIBUTION OF PRUNUS CERASOIDES (WES

DISTRIBUTION OF MECONOPSIS BETONICIFOL

DISTRIBUTION OF MAGNOLIA CAMPBELLII AND